discovering
MATHEMATICS

3B

Chow Wai Keung B. Sc. (Hons), Cert. Ed., M. Soc. Sc.

General Editor: Esther Ng Yoon Cheng B. Sc. (Hons), Dip. Ed.

Consultant: Prof Ling San PhD

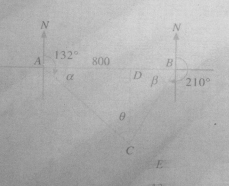

Teacher's Guide

Star Publishing Pte Ltd
115A Commonwealth Drive #05-12
Singapore 149596
Tel: 64796800
Email: contactus@starpub.com.sg

© **Star Publishing Pte Ltd**

ISBN 981-4176-79-6

First published 2007

Printed by CMO Image Printing Enterprise, Singapore

Contents

Acknowledgements

The publisher wishes to thank the following:

The Geometer's Sketchpad, Key Curriculum Press, 1150 65th Street, Emeryville, CA 94608, www.keypress.com for permission to use the screenshots of activities created using The Geometer's Sketchpad.

Week	Topic/Objectives	Strategies	Activities	Resources	Websites
Term 1 Week 1	**Chapter 1 Indices** **1.1 – 1.2 Positive Indices and Laws of Indices, Zero and Negative Integral Indices** • state and apply the laws of indices • state the definitions of zero and negative indices • simplify expressions involving integral indices	Exploring the laws of indices Demonstrating the application of the laws to simplify expressions involving indices Extending the laws of indices to zero and negative integral indices		Chapters 1 to 6 in 3A p.2–6 Textbook p.7–10 Textbook E-Book Teacher's Guide	http://argyll.epsb.ca/jreed/math9/strand1/1104.htm http://www.bbc.co.uk/schools/gcsebitesize/maths/numberih/powersrev2.shtml http://argyll.epsb.ca/jreed/math9/strand1/1201.htm
			p.2 Class Activity 1 p.4 Class Activity 2 p.7 Class Activity 3		
Term 1 Week 2	**1.3 Fractional Indices** • state the definitions of fractional indices • simplify expressions involving fractional indices	Explaining the meaning of the nth root of a number Illustrating by using numerical examples, the relationship between $a^{\frac{1}{n}}$ and the nth root of a positive number Directing the above to the definition of rational indices Demonstrating the skills of simplifying expressions involving fractional indices		p.11–15 Textbook E-Book Teacher's Guide	http://www.bbc.co.uk/schools/gcsebitesize/maths/numberih/powersrev2.shtml

Week	Topic/Objectives	Strategies	Activities	Resources	Websites
Term 1 Week 3	**1.4 –1.5 Standard Form and Comparing Indices** • express numbers in standard form • understand the prefixes in SI units for very large and very small numbers • be aware of rounding and truncation errors in a calculator for very small and very large numbers • solve simple equations involving indices	Discussing the presentation of very large and very small numbers Telling the definition of standard form and the sequence of keying in data into a calculator Conveying examples using the prefixes in SI units for very large and very small numbers Exploring rounding and truncation errors involving very large and very small numbers in calculators Introducing the technique of equating indices to solve equations with numbers having the same base on both sides	p.20 Class Activity 4	p.16–22 Textbook p.22–23 Textbook E-Book Teacher's Guide http://micro.magnet.fsu.edu/primer/java/scienceopticsu/powersof10 p.22; Ex 1.4 (Qn 6) NE Msg 1. (refer to Appendix to SOW)	http://argyll.epsb.ca/jreed/math7/strand1/1103.htm http://www.bbc.co.uk/schools/gcsebitesize/maths/numberih/powersrev1.shtml
Term 1 Week 4	**Chapter 2** **More About Quadratic Equations** **2.1 – 2.2 Factorisation Method and Graphical Method** • solve quadratic equations by factorisation method and graphical method	Revising the method of solving a quadratic equation by factorisation Illustrating the method of solving a quadratic equation by drawing its corresponding graph		p.30–32 Textbook p.32–36 Textbook E-Book Teacher's Guide	http://www.bbc.co.uk/schools/gcsebitesize/maths/activities/flash/snap_factorising.shtml http://www.bbc.co.uk/schools/gcsebitesize/maths/algebraih/quadraticrev1.shtml http://lgfl.skoool.co.uk/viewdetails_ks4.aspx?id=390 http://www.bbc.co.uk/schools/gcsebitesize/maths/activities/intalg_factorising.shtml

Week	Topic/Objectives	Strategies	Activities	Resources	Websites
Term 1 Week 5	**2.3 – 2.4 Completing the Square Method and Quadratic Formula** • solve quadratic equations of the form $x^2 + bx + c = 0$ by the completing the square method • solve quadratic equations by using the quadratic formula	Exploring the idea of completing the square Illustrating the method of solving a quadratic equation by completing the square Deriving the quadratic formula and illustrating how to apply it to solve a quadratic equation	p.37 Class Activity 1	p.36-39 Textbook p.40-42 Textbook E-Book Teacher's Guide	http://lgfl.skoool.co.uk/keystage4.aspx?id=317 http://www.bbc.co.uk/schools/gcsebitesize/maths/activities/flash/snap_factorising/snap_factorising.shtml
Term 1 Week 6	**2.5 – 2.6 Fractional Equations and Problems Involving Quadratic Equations** • solve fractional equations that can be transformed to quadratic equations • apply quadratic equations to solve everyday problems	Extending the method of solving quadratic equations to solve fractional equations that can be transformed to quadratic equations Demonstrating problem solving involving application of quadratic equations		p.43-45 Textbook p.45-50 Textbook E-Book Teacher's Guide	http://lgfl.skoool.co.uk/viewdetails_ks4.aspx?id=390
Term 1 Week 7	**Chapter 3** **Linear Inequalities** **3.1 – 3.2 Basic Properties of Inequalities and Linear Inequalities in One Unknown** • understand the basic properties of inequalities • solve linear inequalities in one unknown • represent the solution of a linear inequality on the number line	Exploring the properties of inequalities Applying the properties to solve linear inequalities in one unknown Illustrating the representation of the solution of an inequality on a number line	p.58 Class Activity 1	p.57-60 Textbook p.60-63 Textbook E-Book Teacher's Guide	http://www.bbc.co.uk/schools/gcsebitesize/maths/activities/intalg_inequalities.shtml http://www.bbc.co.uk/schools/gcsebitesize/maths/algebraih/inequalitiesrev1.shtml

Week	Topic/Objectives	Strategies	Activities	Resources	Websites
Term 1 Week 8	**3.3 – 3.4 Simultaneous Linear Inequalities and Applications of Linear Inequalities** • solve simultaneous linear inequalities in one unknown • apply linear inequalities to solve everyday problems	Explaining the idea of simultaneous inequalities Illustrating different cases of the solution of simultaneous linear inequalities Developing the skill of problem solving involving application of inequalities		p.63-66 Textbook p.66-69 Textbook E-Book Teacher's Guide p.69; Ex 3.4 (Qn 11) NE Msg 6. (refer to Appendix to SOW)	http://www.bbc.co.uk/schools/gcsebitesize/maths/algebraih/inequalitiesrev1.shtml
Term 1 Week 9	**Chapter 4** **Conditions Of Congruence And Similarity** **4.1 – 4.2 Congruent Triangles and Similar Triangles** • state the conditions for two triangles to be congruent • identify congruent triangles • state the conditions for two triangles to be similar	Exploring the conditions for congruent triangles Challenging students to identify congruent triangles and explain their assertion Exploring the conditions for similar triangles	p.76 Class Activity 1 p.78 Class Activity 2 p.80 Class Activity 3 p.86 Class Activity 4 (GSP) p.88 Class Activity 5 (GSP)	p.75-85 Textbook p.85-96 Textbook E-Book Teacher's Guide	http://argyll.epsb.ca/jreed/math9/strand3/3203.htm http://argyll.epsb.ca/jreed/math9/strand3/3201.htm
Term 1 Week 10	**Revision/Exam/Test**				

Week	Topic/Objectives	Strategies	Activities	Resources	Websites
Term 2 Week 1	**4.2 – 4.3 Similar Triangles, Ratio of Areas of Similar Plane Figures** • identify similar triangles • determine whether two plane figures are similar • state the relationship between the ratio of areas and the ratio of lengths of two similar plane figures	Prompting students to identify similar triangles and write down the reasons for similarity Illustrating the applications of similar triangles to find unknown sides and angles Exploring the relationship between the ratio of the corresponding sides of similar plane figures and the ratio of their areas	p.90 Class Activity 6 (GSP) p.96 Class Activity 7	p.85-96 Textbook p.96-101 Textbook E-Book Teacher's Guide	http://argyll.epsb.ca/jreed/math9/strand3/3201.htm http://standards.nctm.org/document/eexamples/chap6/6.3/index.htm
Term 2 Week 2	**4.3 – 4.4 Ratio of Areas of Similar Plane Figures, Ratio of Volumes of Similar Solids** • apply the above property to solve problems • determine whether two solids are similar • state the relationship between the ratio of volumes and the ratio of lengths of two similar solids • apply the above property to solve problems	Demonstrating how to use the above relationship to solve application problems Exploring the relationship between the ratio of the corresponding sides of two similar solids and the ratio of their volumes Employing the above relationship to solve application problems	p.102 Class Activity 8	p.96-101 Textbook p.102-107 Textbook E-Book Teacher's Guide	http://argyll.epsb.ca/jreed/math9/strand3/3201.htm http://standards.nctm.org/document/eexamples/chap6/6.3/index.htm

Week	Topic/Objectives	Strategies	Activities	Resources	Websites
Term 2 Week 3	**Chapter 5 Functions And Graphs** **5.1 Graph Sketching of Quadratic Functions** • sketch the graphs of quadratic functions of the forms: $y = \pm(x - h)^2 + k$ and $y = \pm(x - p)(x - q)$	Exploring the features of the quadratic graph of the forms: $y = \pm(x - h)^2 + k$ and $y = \pm(x - p)(x - q)$. Developing students' habit of observing the turning point, x- and y-intercepts, and the line of symmetry of a quadratic graph	p.118 Class Activity 1 (GSP)	p.117-125 Textbook E-Book Teacher's Guide http://www.univie.ac.at/future.media/moe/tests/fun1/erkennen.html Chapter 5 opener; NE Msg 6. (refer to Appendix to SOW)	http://www.bbc.co.uk/schools/gcsebitesize/maths/activities/quad_graphs.shtml http://argyll.epsb.ca/jreed/math7/strand2/2102.htm http://nlvm.usu.edu/en/nav/frames_asid_109_g_3_t_1.html?open=activities
Term 2 Week 4	**5.2 Graphs of Power Functions** • draw the graph of the function $y = ax^n$ for $n = -2, -1, 0, 1, 2$ and 3	Illustrating the techniques of drawing the graphs of power functions Discussing the features of power functions		p.125-131 Textbook E-Book Teacher's Guide	http://www.bbc.co.uk/schools/gcsebitesize/maths/activities/flash/proportion_graphs/proportion_graphs.shtml http://nlvm.usu.edu/en/nav/frames_asid_109_g_3_t_1.html?open=activities
Term 2 Week 5	**5.3 Graphs of Sums of Power Functions** • draw the graph of the sum of not more than 3 functions of the form $y = ax^n$ for $n = -2, -1, 0, 1, 2$ and 3	Developing students' skill in drawing the graphs of sums of power functions Exploring various combinations of power functions; graphing software may be employed		p.131-135 Textbook E-Book Teacher's Guide	http://nlvm.usu.edu/en/nav/frames_asid_109_g_3_t_1.html?open=activities http://www.bbc.co.uk/schools/gcsebitesize/maths/activities/flash/proportion_graphs/proportion_graphs.shtml

Week	Topic/Objectives	Strategies	Activities	Resources	Websites
Term 2 Week 6	**5.4 – 5.5 Graphs of Exponential Functions and Gradients of Curves** • draw the graph of an exponential function $y = ka^x$, where a is a positive integer • estimate the gradient of a curve by drawing a tangent to the curve	Illustrating the features of exponential functions Describing the idea of tangent Demonstrating the technique of finding the gradient of a graph by drawing a tangent		p.135-139 Textbook p.139-146 Textbook E-Book Teacher's Guide	http://nlvm.usu.edu/en/nav/frames_asid_109_g_3_t_1.html?open=activities http://argyll.epsb.ca/jreed/math7/strand2/2102.htm
Term 2 Weeks 7-9	Revision/Exam/Test				
Term 3 Week 1	**Chapter 6** **Properties Of Circles** **6.1 – 6.2 Chords of a Circle, Angles in a Circle** • recognise equal chords are equidistant from the centre • recognise the perpendicular bisector of a chord passes through the centre of a circle • apply the above properties to solve problems • recognise the angle at the centre is twice the angle at the circumference • recognise an angle in a semicircle is a right angle • recognise the angles in the same segment are equal	Exploring the properties of chords in a circle Using examples to show how to apply those properties Encouraging students to write down the reasons for steps in their workings Exploring the properties of angles in a circle Grouping students and asking them whether they can present some proofs for the properties	p.159 Class Activity 1 (GSP) p.161 Class Activity 2 (GSP) p.164 Class Activity 3 (GSP) p.169 Class Activity 4 (GSP) p.173 Class Activity 5 (GSP)	p.158-168 Textbook p.168-178 Textbook E-Book Teacher's Guide	www.mathsnet.net/dynamic/circle1.html www.mathsnet.net/dynamic/circle2.html www.mathsnet.net/dynamic/circle3.html

Week	Topic/Objectives	Strategies	Activities	Resources	Websites
Term 3 Week 2	**6.2 – 6.3 Angles in a Circle, Angles in the Opposite Segments** • apply the above properties to solve problems • state the properties of angles in opposite segments	Demonstrating the applications of the properties to solve problems Exploring the property of angles in the opposite segments Showing the applications of the above property in problem solving	p.179 Class Activity 6 (GSP)	p.168-178 Textbook p.179-184 Textbook E-Book Teacher's Guide	www.mathsnet.net/ dynamic/circle1.html www.mathsnet.net/ dynamic/circle2.html www.mathsnet.net/ dynamic/circle3.html
Term 3 Week 3	**6.4 Tangents to a Circle** • draw a tangent to a circle • understand that a tangent to a circle is perpendicular to the radius of the circle at the point of contact • apply the above properties to solve problems • recognise tangents from an external point are equal in length • recognise the line joining an external point to the centre of a circle bisects the angle between the tangents from the external point • apply the above properties to solve problems	Conveying the idea of tangent to a circle Exploring the properties of tangents from an external point to a circle Illustrating how to use those properties to solve problems	p.187 Class Activity 7 (GSP)	p.184-192 Textbook E-Book Teacher's Guide	http://www.gcseguide. co.uk/circle_theorems. htm http://www.mathsrevision. net/gcse/pages. php?page=13

Week	Topic/Objectives	Strategies	Activities	Resources	Websites
Term 3 Week 4	**Chapter 7 Trigonometry** **7.1 Trigonometric Ratios of Acute Angles** • state the definitions of trigonometric ratios of sine, cosine and tangent for acute angles • find a trigonometric ratio from a right-angled triangle • obtain the values of trigonometric ratios from a calculator • use the trigonometric ratios to calculate unknown sides and angles in a right-angled triangle	Defining the trigonometric ratios sine, cosine and tangent for acute angles Demonstrating how to use a calculator to find the values of trigonometric ratios, and how to find the value of an angle when the value of a trigonometric ratio of the angle is given Developing the skill of using trigonometric ratios to solve problems	p.2 Class Activity 1	Chapters 7 to 11 in 3B p.2-5 Textbook p.5-12 Textbook E-Book Teacher's Guide	http://lgfl.skoool. co.uk/viewdetails_ks3. aspx?id=562 http://lgfl.skoool. co.uk/viewdetails_ks3. aspx?id=561 http://www.bbc.co.uk/ schools/gcsebitesize/ maths/activities/ trigonometry.shtml http://lgfl.skoool.co.uk/ keystage4.aspx?id=317
Term 3 Week 5	**7.2 – 7.3 Trigonometric Ratios of Obtuse Angles and Formula for the Area of a Triangle** • state the definitions of sine and cosine functions for obtuse angles • find the values of sine and cosine for obtuse angles • find the area of a triangle using the formula: $Area = \frac{1}{2}bc \sin A$	Extending the definitions of sine and cosine to obtuse angles Exploring the area formula of triangle, $Area = \frac{1}{2}bc \sin A$ Demonstrating the applications of the above formula	p.19 Class Activity 2	p.13-18 Textbook p.18-24 Textbook E-Book Teacher's Guide http://aleph0.clarku. edu/~djoyce/java/trig/ area.html	http://lgfl.skoool.co.uk/ keystage4.aspx?id=317 http://www.nipissingu. ca/calculus/tutorials/ trigonometry.html

Week	Topic/Objectives	Strategies	Activities	Resources	Websites
Week 3 Week 6	**7.4 – 7.5 The Sine Rule and The Cosine Rule** • state the sine rule • apply the sine rule to solve problems • state the cosine rule • apply the cosine rule to solve problems	Deriving the sine rule using the area of a triangle Demonstrating the applications of the sine rule to solve problems, including the ambiguous case Deriving the formula of the cosine rule Demonstrating the applications of the cosine rule to solve problems		p.25-32 Textbook p.32-38 Textbook E-Book Teacher's Guide p.38; Ex 7.5 (Qn 16) NE Msg 1. (refer to Appendix to SOW)	http://lgfl.skoool.co.uk/keystage4.aspx?id=317 http://www.bbc.co.uk/schools/gcsebitesize/maths/shapeh/areaofatrianglerev1.shtml http://www.mathsrevision.net/gcse/pages.php?page=40
Term 3 Week 7	**Chapter 8 Applications Of Trigonometry** **8.1 – 8.2 Bearing Problems, Angles of Elevation and Depression** • solve problems involving bearings and navigation • understand the idea of angles of elevation and depression • solve problems involving angles of elevation and depression	Discussing the measurement of bearings Applying the trigonometric rules to solve bearing problems Introducing the idea of angles of elevation and depression Demonstrating the skills in solving problems involving angles of elevation and depression		p.46-52 Textbook p.53-57 Textbook E-Book Teacher's Guide Chapter 8 opener; NE Msg 1. (refer to Appendix to SOW)	www.active-maths.co.uk/whiteboard/3measure/meas_bearing1.html http://www.algebralab.org/Word/Word.aspx?file=Trigonometry_AnglesElevDepression.xml
Term 3 Week 8	**8.3 Simple Three-Dimensional Problems** • apply trigonometry to solve simple 3-dimensional problems in our daily life	Using 3D models to illustrate the relationships of sides and angles in different planes Building up students' 3D spatial concept using examples		p.57-63 Textbook E-Book Teacher's Guide	http://resources.emb.gov.hk/trigo/#

Week	Topic/Objectives	Strategies	Activities	Resources	Websites
Term 3 Week 9	**Chapter 9** **Coordinate Geometry** **9.1 – 9.2 Length of a Line Segment and Gradient of a Straight Line** • find the length of a line segment on a coordinate plane • find the gradient of a straight line given the coordinates of two points on it	Exploring the distance formula for a line segment on a coordinate plane Demonstrating the applications of the formula Deriving the formula for the gradient of a straight line Applying the formula to find the gradients of lines in various positions	p.73 Class Activity 1	p.73-79 Textbook p.79-84 Textbook E-Book Teacher's Guide	www.active-maths. co.uk/whiteboard/3geom/ 2points_pythag.html http://argyll.epsb.ca/jreed/ math7/strand2/2102.htm
Term 3 Week 10	**Revision/Exam/Test**				
Term 4 Week 1	**9.3 Equation of a Straight Line** • interpret and find the equation of a straight line graph in the form $y = mx + c$ • solve geometric problems involving the use of coordinates	Introducing the gradient-intercept form of a straight line Demonstrating the technique of obtaining the equation of a straight line from the above form when sufficient conditions are given		p.84-89 Textbook E-Book Teacher's Guide http://www.shodor.org/ interactivate/activities/ slopeslider/index.html	http://argyll.epsb.ca/jreed/ math7/strand2/2102.htm http://www.math.com/ school/subject2/lessons/ S2U4L2GL.html

Week	Topic/Objectives	Strategies	Activities	Resources	Websites
Term 4 Week 2	**Chapter 10 Arc Lengths And Sector Areas** **10.1 – 10.2 Arc Lengths, Sector Areas and Segment Areas** • understand the relationship between arc length and angle subtended by arc • understand the relationship between sector area of a circle and angle subtended by arc • calculate the arc length and sector area of a circle • calculate the area of a segment	Exploring the relationship between the length of an arc and its angle subtending at the centre of the circle Applying the above relationship to solve application problems Exploring the relationship between the area of a sector and the angle at the centre of the sector Applying the above relationship to find the areas of sectors and the areas of segments	p.96 Class Activity 1 (GSP) p.102 Class Activity 2 (GSP)	p.96-101 Textbook p.102-107 Textbook E-Book Teacher's Guide	http://library.thinkquest.org/C0110248/geometry/menareasect.htm http://www.coolmath.com/reference/circles-geometry.html http://www.bbc.co.uk/schools/gcsebitesize/maths/shapeih/circlesandglesarcsandsectorsrev3.shtml
Term 4 Week 3	**10.3 – 10.4 Radian Measure, Formulae in Radian Measure** • understand radian measure of angle • convert between radians and degrees • express arc length and sector area formulae using radian measure • apply the formulae to solve problems	Describing the definition of radian Showing the conversion between radians and degrees Deriving the formulae for the arc length and sector area when the angle at centre is in radians Demonstrating the applications of the above formulae in solving problems		p.107-112 Textbook p.113-118 Textbook E-Book Teacher's Guide	http://library.thinkquest.org/C0110248/geometry/radian_de.htm http://www.themathpage.com/aTrig/arc-length.htm http://library.thinkquest.org/C0110248/geometry/radian_arc.htm http://library.thinkquest.org/C0110248/geometry/radian_sect.htm

Week	Topic/Objectives	Strategies	Activities	Resources	Websites
Term 4 Week 4	**Chapter 11** **Quartiles And Percentiles** **11.1 – 11.2 Cumulative Frequency Diagrams and Range, Quartiles, Interquartile Range and Percentiles** • understand the term cumulative frequency • recognise features of cumulative frequency curves • interpret and analyse cumulative frequency curves • understand the terms range, quartiles, interquartile range and percentiles	Conveying the concept of cumulative frequency through an activity Demonstrating the construction of a cumulative frequency curve Developing students' skill in interpreting and analysing cumulative frequency curves Explaining the concept of spread of data and its measurements Introducing the terms range, quartiles, interquartile range and percentile	p. 126 Class Activity 1	p.126-133 Textbook p.134-147 Textbook E-Book Teacher's Guide	http://www.bbc.co.uk/schools/gcsebitesize/maths/activities/cumulative_frequency.shtml http://www.bbc.co.uk/schools/gcsebitesize/maths/datahandlingih/scatterdiagramsirev3.shtml
Term 4 Week 5	**11.2 – 11.3 Range, Quartiles, Interquartile Range and Percentiles, and Box-and-Whisker Plots** • find the values of the above terms from a distribution • recognise the features of a box-and-whisker plot • interpret and analyse box-and-whisker plots	Demonstrating the technique to find the above measures from ungrouped data and grouped data Explaining the features of a box-and-whisker plot through the construction of such diagram Developing students' skill in interpreting and analysing box-and-whisker plots		p.147-155 Textbook E-Book Teacher's Guide	http://www.bbc.co.uk/schools/gcsebitesize/maths/datahandlingih/scatterdiagramsirev3.shtml http://nlvm.usu.edu/en/nav/frames_asid_200_g_3_t_5.html?open=instructions
Term 4 Weeks 6–7	**Revision/ Exam**				

APPENDIX TO SCHEME OF WORK

National Education Messages

NE MSG 1	Singapore is our homeland; this is where we belong.
	We want to keep our heritage and our way of life.
NE MSG 2	We must preserve racial and religious harmony.
	Though many races, religions, languages and cultures, we pursue one destiny.
NE MSG 3	We must uphold meritocracy and incorruptibility.
	This means opportunity for all, according to their ability and effort.
NE MSG 4	No one owes Singapore a living.
	We must find our own way to survive and prosper.
NE MSG 5	We must ourselves defend Singapore.
	No one else is responsible for our security and well-being.
NE MSG 6	We have confidence in our future.
	United, determined and well-prepared, we shall build a bright future for ourselves.

Notes On Teaching

Chapter 7   Trigonometry

Suggested Approach

Trigonometry is new to students and it is worthwhile spending more time on this topic. It is suggested that teachers teach this chapter after students have achieved a good foundation in geometry and mensuration. The emphasis is on the understanding of trigonometric ratios and their practical aspects in finding angles and lengths of objects and in navigation. An in-depth treatment of the properties of trigonometric functions is not expected.

We first define trigonometric ratios for acute angles and use some simple applications to consolidate their concept. After that, the definitions of sine and cosine ratios (not tangent ratio) are extended to obtuse angles. This is to facilitate discussion on the sine rule and the cosine rule later.

Students should recognise the conditions for fixing a triangle. As a motivating activity, students can be asked to solve a non-right-angled triangle before the introduction of the sine rule and the cosine rule. Then they should note that applying the sine rule and the cosine rule together is more than sufficient to solve any triangle, provided sufficient information is given. More application problems of these rules can reinforce their concept.

7.1   Trigonometric Ratios Of Acute Angles

We may use the lengths of the three sides of a right-angled triangle to define the trigonometric ratios sine, cosine and tangent of an acute angle. Examples of using a calculator to get the values of trigonometric ratios and to find an angle with a given value of a trigonometric ratio can also be demonstrated. Abler students can explore how the values of the trigonometric ratios change as the corresponding angle varies. Sufficient simple applications of using these ratios to solve a right-angled triangle may enhance students' understanding of these ratios.

7.2   Trigonometric Ratios Of Obtuse Angles

We may use the coordinates (x, y) of a point on a circle with the centre at the origin and radius r to define the trigonometric ratios: sine and cosine of an obtuse angle. Students should recognise the signs of these ratios in the first and second quadrants.

7.3   Formula For The Area Of A Triangle

The area formula of a triangle, $\frac{1}{2} bc \sin A$ for a triangle ABC, is applicable for any two sides and the included angle. We should also demonstrate to students that the formula is valid for both acute and obtuse angle A.

7.4   The Sine Rule

There are several methods, including the use of the area of a triangle as illustrated in the book, to derive the sine rule. In an ambiguous case, it is better to illustrate it with the aid of separate diagrams. Teachers should note that when applying the sine rule to find an angle, many students may omit to include or forget to check the case for the obtuse angle.

7.5   The Cosine Rule

It is not necessary to memorise how the cosine rule is derived. For the two forms of the cosine rule, it is advisable to introduce them one at a time, with an adequate number of immediate examples and exercises. This should serve to consolidate their understanding of the rule.

Chapter 8   Applications Of Trigonometry

Suggested Approach

The focus of this chapter is on applying trigonometry to solve problems involving bearing, angles of elevation and depression, and some simple 3D situations. 3D models, both physical models and computer simulation models, are all good teaching aids for this topic.

Students should have the habit of writing down the subsequent steps for the solution of the problems.

8.1   Bearing Problems

Here we introduce the true bearing system. Students might find it more interesting if some compasses are provided in the class. Activities involving finding the relative bearings between the positions of students can also be provided.

8.2   Angles Of Elevation And Depression

Students may be asked to suggest a method of finding inaccessible heights using the angle of elevation. Some students may wrongly assume that the angle of depression is the angle between the line of sight and the vertical.

8.3   Simple Three Dimensional Problems

Students have to develop the ability to visualise 3D objects through practice. They should be guided to analyse 3D diagrams and resolve them into related 2D figures. They should be advised to draw diagrams clearly. The calculation of the angle between two lines and the angle between a line and a plane is not expected.

Chapter 9   Coordinate Geometry

Suggested Approach

Teachers could guide students in discovering the formula for the distance of two points on a coordinate plane. Some activities can be used to bridge the definition of the gradient of a line, "rise over run", to the gradient formula. It is not necessary to mention the conditions for parallel lines and perpendicular lines.

We may use the intuitive approach to introduce the gradient-intercept form of a straight line. Using the gradient-intercept form, students should be able to find the equation of a straight line when a point on the line and the gradient of the line are given, or when two points on the line are given.

As an application, they may be asked to prove some geometric properties using the materials learned in this chapter.

9.1   *Length Of A Line Segment*

The formula for the length of a line segment may be considered as an application of Pythagoras' theorem. Initially, students may be asked to find the distance between two horizontal points and the distance between two vertical points. It would then be easier for them to discover the formula by themselves. They may be reminded to leave the intermediate answers of distances in surd form, if appropriate, and asked to give the final answers correct to 3 significant figures.

9.2   *Gradient Of A Straight Line*

Students should note that any two points chosen on a straight line will give the same value for the gradient of the line. In applying the formula, it does not matter which point is taken first. Students should be reminded that the gradient of a vertical line is undefined.

9.3   *Equation Of A Straight Line*

Students are expected to apply the gradient-intercept form to find the equation of a straight line from various given conditions. They should also be able to find the gradient and intercepts of a line in the form $ax + by + c = 0$.

Chapter 10 Arc Lengths and Sector Areas

Suggested Approach

Students may use Sketchpad to find out that the arc length and area of sector are proportional to the angle subtended at the centre by the arc. They can then be led to derive the formulae of arc length and area of sector. A variety of application problems can reinforce students' mastery of the concept.

They should understand the meaning of radian and recognise its use in further mathematics. They should attempt to switch between the degree mode and the radian mode in a calculator, and hence find the trigonometric ratios for angles in different units.

10.1 Arc Lengths

Students should differentiate between the terms segment and the sector of a circle. We must use three points to describe a major arc. In applying the arc length formula, students should make sure that $x°$ is the measure of the angle at the centre subtended by the arc, not the angle at the circumference.

10.2 Surface Areas And Segment Areas

The formula for the surface area of a sector is derived using the proportional property. It may not be necessary for students to memorise any formula for the area of a segment. They should, instead, use the fact that the area of a segment is equal to the area of a sector minus the area of the triangle formed by the chord of the segment and the two corresponding radii.

10.3 Radian Measure

Some students may have difficulty in understanding the concept of radian. Teachers would need some care and effort to ensure that students learn the concept well. Students could be asked to draw angles of 1, 1.5, 2, 2.5 radians in order to appreciate the magnitudes of angles in radians.

10.4 Formulae In Radian Measure

Students should appreciate the simplicity of the formulae of arc length and area of sector, when the angle at the centre is in radians. However, they should make sure that the angle is in radians when applying the formulae. Exercises on perimeters and areas of composite figures involving arcs and sectors can help students to consolidate what they have learnt.

Chapter 11   Quartiles and Percentiles

Suggested Approach

The emphasis is on teaching the cumulative frequency diagram and the box-and-whisker plot to analyse and interpret these diagrams. Teachers may prepare a variety of such diagrams beforehand for class discussion. Questions could be asked about what information is conveyed by the diagrams.

To introduce the idea of spread of data, students may be asked to compare two sets of data with the same mean and median but with a different spread. They should realise that, apart from describing a data set by a measure of central tendency, there is a need to have a measure of the spread of data.

Different types of measures of spread can be discussed and illustrated with some daily life examples. Students could be encouraged to discuss the advantages and disadvantages of each type of measure.

11.1   *Cumulative Frequency Diagrams*

Students may be asked to prepare a cumulative frequency table and draw a cumulative frequency curve from a frequency table. Teachers may guide them to discuss what conclusions can be drawn from a cumulative frequency curve. Students have to observe the title, the legends and the scales on both axes of a cumulative frequency curve.

11.2   *Range, Quartiles, Interquartile Range And Percentiles*

Students should be reminded that the definitions of range and quartiles are different for ungrouped data and grouped data. They are required to find the quartiles and percentiles of a distribution from its cumulative frequency curve. Some students may have the wrong notion that $\frac{N}{4}$ is the lower quartile.

11.3   *Box-And-Whisker Plots*

Students should note the general appearance of a box-and-whisker plot. They should understand its use in displaying the characteristics of a data set. They are expected to compare two different data sets using box-and-whisker plots.

FULLY

WORKED

SOLUTIONS

Chapter 7   Trigonometry

Class Activity 1

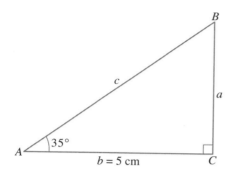 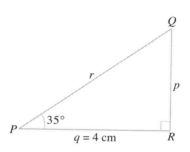

1. Draw $\triangle ABC$ and $\triangle PQR$ as shown above in which $\angle A = \angle P = 35°$, $\angle C = \angle R = 90°$, $b = 5$ cm and $q = 4$ cm.

2. Is $\triangle ABC$ similar to $\triangle PQR$?

    Yes, $\triangle ABC$ is similar to $\triangle PQR$ (AAA similarity).

3. Measure a, c, p and r.

    $a =$ _____3.5 cm_____ , $c =$ _____6.1 cm_____ ,

    $p =$ _____2.8 cm_____ , $r =$ _____4.9 cm_____ .

4. Calculate the following ratios, correct to 2 significant figures.

    (a) $\dfrac{a}{c}$ and $\dfrac{p}{r}$: $\dfrac{a}{c} =$ _____$\dfrac{3.5}{6.1} = 0.57$_____ , $\dfrac{p}{r} =$ _____$\dfrac{2.8}{4.9} = 0.57$_____ .

    (b) $\dfrac{b}{c}$ and $\dfrac{q}{r}$: $\dfrac{b}{c} =$ _____$\dfrac{5}{6.1} = 0.82$_____ , $\dfrac{q}{r} =$ _____$\dfrac{4}{4.9} = 0.82$_____ .

    (c) $\dfrac{a}{b}$ and $\dfrac{p}{q}$: $\dfrac{a}{b} =$ _____$\dfrac{3.5}{5} = 0.7$_____ , $\dfrac{p}{q} =$ _____$\dfrac{2.8}{4} = 0.7$_____ .

5. Write down a conclusion about each pair of ratios in questions **4(a)**, **4(b)** and **4(c)**.

    The ratios in each pair are equal.

Class Activity 2

Copy the following working and fill in the boxes with appropriate expressions.

1. Suppose $\triangle ABC$ has sides $AC = 15$ cm and $AB = 13$ cm, and the included angle $A = 50°$.

We drop a perpendicular from B to AC.
In $\triangle ABD$,

$$\frac{h}{13} = \sin 50°$$

$$\therefore \qquad h = 13 \times \underline{\quad \sin 50° \quad}$$

$$\text{Area of } \triangle ABC = \frac{1}{2} \times \underline{\quad 15 \quad} \times h$$

$$= \frac{1}{2} \times \underline{\quad 15 \quad} \times \underline{\quad 13 \quad} \times \underline{\quad \sin 50° \quad} \text{ cm}^2$$

$$\approx \underline{\quad 74.7 \quad} \text{ cm}^2$$

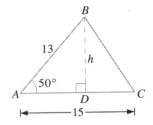

2. Suppose $\triangle ABC$ has sides $AC = 25$ cm and $AB = 23$ cm, and the included angle $A = 115°$.

We drop a perpendicular from B to CA produced.
In $\triangle ABD$,

$$\angle BAD = 180° - 115° = 65°$$

$$\frac{h}{23} = \sin \underline{\quad \angle BAD \quad}$$

$$h = 23 \times \underline{\quad \sin 65° \quad}$$

$$\text{Area of } \triangle ABC = \frac{1}{2} \times \underline{\quad 25 \quad} \times h$$

$$= \frac{1}{2} \times \underline{\quad 25 \quad} \times \underline{\quad 23 \quad} \times \underline{\quad \sin 65° \quad} \text{ cm}^2$$

$$\approx \underline{\quad 260.6 \quad} \text{ cm}^2$$

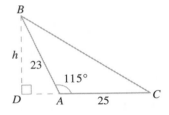

3. Consider the general case of a triangle with sides b, c and $\angle A$ given, where $\angle A$ is acute.

$$h = c \times \underline{\quad \sin A \quad}$$

$$\therefore \quad \text{area of } \triangle ABC = \frac{1}{2} \times \underline{\quad b \quad} \times h$$

$$= \underline{\quad \frac{1}{2}\,bc \sin A \quad}$$

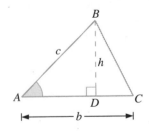

4. Consider the general case of a triangle with sides b, c and $\angle A$ given, where $\angle A$ is obtuse.

$$h = c \times \underline{\quad \sin \quad}(180° - A)$$

$$= c \times \underline{\quad \sin \quad} A$$

$$\therefore \quad \text{area of } \triangle ABC = \frac{1}{2} \times \underline{\quad b \quad} \times h$$

$$= \underline{\quad \frac{1}{2}\,bc \sin A \quad}$$

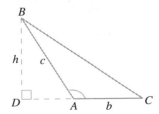

Extend Your Learning Curve

Trigonometric Identities

Since trigonometric ratios are defined as the ratios of any two sides of a right-angled triangle, or generally, as the ratio between two values from x, y and r of a point $P(x, y)$ on a circle of radius r and with the centre at the origin, they are closely related to one another. Let us investigate what their relationships are.

(a) Complete the following table, giving the values correct to 4 decimal places.

θ	20°	30°	45°	60°	80°	100°
$\sin \theta$						
$\cos \theta$						
$\tan \theta$						
$\sin 2\theta$						
$\cos 2\theta$						
$\sin^2 \theta$						
$\cos^2 \theta$						
$\sin^2 \theta + \cos^2 \theta$						
$\cos^2 \theta - \sin^2 \theta$						
$\sin \theta \cos \theta$						
$\dfrac{\sin \theta}{\cos \theta}$						

(b) Write down some conjectures about the relationships of the trigonometric expressions in the above table.

Solution

(a)

θ	20°	30°	45°	60°	80°	100°
$\sin \theta$	0.3420	0.5	0.7071	0.8660	0.9848	0.9848
$\cos \theta$	0.9397	0.8660	0.7071	0.5	0.1736	−0.1736
$\tan \theta$	0.3640	0.5774	1	1.7321	5.6713	−5.6713
$\sin 2\theta$	0.6428	0.8660	1	0.8660	0.3420	−0.3420
$\cos 2\theta$	0.7660	0.5	0	−0.5	−0.9397	−0.9397
$\sin^2 \theta$	0.1170	0.25	0.5000	0.7500	0.9698	0.9698
$\cos^2 \theta$	0.8830	0.7500	0.5000	0.25	0.0302	0.0302
$\sin^2 \theta + \cos^2 \theta$	1.0000	1.0000	1.0000	1.0000	1.0000	1.0000
$\cos^2 \theta - \sin^2 \theta$	0.7660	0.5	0	−0.5	−0.9397	−0.9397
$\sin \theta \cos \theta$	0.3214	0.4330	0.5	0.4330	0.1710	−0.1710
$\dfrac{\sin \theta}{\cos \theta}$	0.3640	0.5774	1	1.7321	5.6713	−5.6713

(b) We observe that
1. $\sin^2 \theta + \cos^2 \theta = 1$,
2. $\tan \theta = \dfrac{\sin \theta}{\cos \theta}$,
3. $\cos 2\theta = \cos^2 \theta - \sin^2 \theta$,
4. $\sin 2\theta = 2 \sin \theta \cos \theta$.

Try It!

Section 7.1

1. Find the values of the following, giving your answers correct to 4 significant figures.
   - **(a)** sin 47°
   - **(b)** cos 25.3°
   - **(d)** tan 79°
   - **(d)** sin 20° + sin 27°

   #### Solution
   - **(a)** sin 47° = 0.7314   (correct to 4 sig. fig.)
   - **(b)** cos 25.3° = 0.9041   (correct to 4 sig. fig.)
   - **(c)** tan 79° = 5.145   (correct to 4 sig. fig.)
   - **(d)** sin 20° + sin 27° = 0.7960 (correct to 4 sig. fig.)

2. Find the angle θ in degrees in each of the following, giving your answer correct to 1 decimal place.
   - **(a)** sin θ = 0.258
   - **(b)** cos θ = 0.9715
   - **(c)** tan θ = 3.009
   - **(d)** sin θ = 1.463

   #### Solution
   - **(a)** sin θ = 0.258
     θ = 15.0°   (correct to 1 d.p.)
   - **(b)** cos θ = 0.9715
     θ = 13.7°   (correct to 1 d.p.)
   - **(c)** tan θ = 3.009
     θ = 71.6°   (correct to 1 d.p.)
   - **(d)** sin θ = 1.463
     There is no solution for θ.

3. In the diagram, PR = 9 cm, $\angle P$ = 60° and $\angle Q$ = 90°. Find the lengths of QR and PQ.

   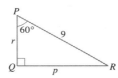

   #### Solution
   $$\sin 60° = \frac{p}{9}$$
   $$p = 9 \sin 60°$$
   $$= 7.79 \quad \text{(correct to 3 sig. fig.)}$$
   $$\cos 60° = \frac{r}{9}$$
   $$r = 9 \cos 60°$$
   $$= 4.5$$
   $\therefore$ QR = 7.79 cm and PQ = 4.5 cm.

4. In the diagram, PN = 17 cm, $\angle M$ = 53° and $\angle P$ = 90°. Find the lengths of MN and PM.

   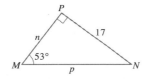

Solution
$$\frac{17}{p} = \sin 53°$$
$$p = \frac{17}{\sin 53°}$$
$$= 21.3 \quad \text{(correct to 3 sig. fig.)}$$
$$\frac{17}{n} = \tan 53°$$
$$n = \frac{17}{\tan 53°}$$
$$= 12.8 \quad \text{(correct to 3 sig. fig.)}$$
$\therefore$ MN = 21.3 cm and PM = 12.8 cm.

5. In the diagram, $PQRS$ is a rectangle, PQ = 30 cm and PS = 23 cm. Find
   - **(a)** the angle between the diagonal QS and the side PS,
   - **(b)** the length of QS.

   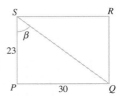

   #### Solution
   - **(a)** $\tan \beta = \dfrac{30}{23}$
     β = 52.52°
     = 52.5°   (correct to 1 d.p.)
   - **(b)** $\sin \beta = \dfrac{30}{QS}$
     $QS = \dfrac{30}{\sin 52.52°}$
     = 37.8 cm   (correct to 3 sig. fig.)

6. In $\triangle PQR$, PQ = PR = 9 cm and QR = 16 cm. Find $\angle PQR$.

   #### Solution

   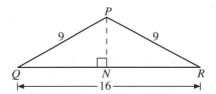

   $\triangle PQR$ is isosceles and hence PN bisects QR.

   In $\triangle PQN$, $QN = \dfrac{1}{2} \times 16$
   $$= 8 \text{ cm}$$
   $$\cos \angle PQR = \frac{QN}{PQ}$$
   $$= \frac{8}{9}$$
   $\therefore$ $\angle PQR$ = 27.3°   (correct to 1 d.p.)

7. In the diagram, $\angle RPQ = 34°$, $\angle RQP = 90°$, $RQ = 12$ cm and $PS = 10$ cm. Find

(a) the length of QS,

(b) the angle β.

Solution

(a) In $\triangle PQR$,

$$\tan 34° = \frac{RQ}{PQ} = \frac{12}{PQ}$$

$$PQ = \frac{12}{\tan 34°}$$
$$= 17.7907 \text{ cm}$$
$$QS = PQ - PS$$
$$= 17.7907 - 10$$
$$= 7.7907$$
$$= 7.79 \text{ cm} \quad \text{(correct to 3 sig. fig.)}$$

(b) In $\triangle SQR$,

$$\tan \angle SRQ = \frac{QS}{RQ}$$
$$= \frac{7.7907}{12}$$
$$\angle SRQ = 32.99°$$
$$34° + \beta + 32.99° + 90° = 180° \quad (\angle \text{ sum of } \triangle)$$
$$\therefore \quad \beta = 23.01°$$
$$= 23.0°$$

(correct to 1 d.p.)

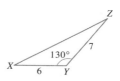

Section 7.2

8. Find the values of sin 130° and cos 130° by constructing the angle on a coordinate plane.

Solution

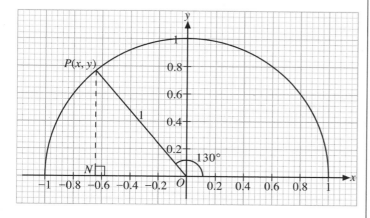

In the figure, $\angle xOP = 130°$.
$$x = -0.64 \text{ and } y = 0.76.$$
$$\therefore \text{ from the graph,} \quad \sin 130° = y = 0.76$$
$$\cos 130° = x = -0.64$$

9. Express the following as trigonometric ratios of acute angles and find their values correct to 4 significant figures.
(a) sin 168°
(b) cos 96°

Solution

(a) $\sin 168° = \sin (180° - 12°)$
$$= \sin 12°$$
$$= 0.2079 \quad \text{(correct to 4 sig. fig.)}$$

(b) $\cos 96° = \cos (180° - 84°)$
$$= -\cos 84°$$
$$= -0.1045 \quad \text{(correct to 4 sig. fig.)}$$

10. If $0° \le \theta \le 180°$, find the possible values of θ when
(a) $\sin \theta = 0.7$,
(b) $\cos \theta = -0.625$.

Solution

(a) $\sin \theta = 0.7$
$$\theta = 44.4° \text{ or } (180° - 44.4°)$$
$$= 44.4° \text{ or } 135.6° \quad \text{(correct to 1 d.p.)}$$

(b) $\cos \theta = -0.625$
$$\theta = 128.7° \quad \text{(correct to 1 d.p.)}$$

Section 7.3

11. In $\triangle XYZ$, $XY = 6$ cm, $YZ = 7$ cm and $\angle XYZ = 130°$. Find the area of $\triangle XYZ$.

Solution

Area of $\triangle XYZ = \frac{1}{2} \times 6 \times 7 \times \sin 130°$
$$= 16.1 \text{ cm}^2 \quad \text{(correct to 3 sig. fig.)}$$

12. In $\triangle ABC$, $BC = 9$ cm, $CA = 7$ cm and the area of $\triangle ABC$ is 28 cm². Find $\angle ACB$.

Solution

$$\frac{1}{2} \times 9 \times 7 \times \sin \angle ACB = 28$$
$$\sin \angle ACB = \frac{8}{9}$$
$$\angle ACB = 62.7° \text{ or } (180° - 62.7°)$$
$$= 62.7° \text{ or } 117.3° \quad \text{(correct to 1 d.p.)}$$

13. (a) A regular hexagon is inscribed in a circle of radius 6 cm. Find the area of the hexagon.

(b) In the figure, $PQRS$ is a parallelogram, $PQ = 2x$ cm, $QR = x$ cm and $\angle PQR = 110°$. If the parallelogram and the hexagon in **(a)** have the same area, find the value of x.

Solution

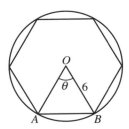

(a) $\theta = \dfrac{360°}{6} = 60°$

Area of $\triangle AOB = \dfrac{1}{2} \times 6 \times 6 \times \sin 60°$

$\therefore$ area of the hexagon

$= 6 \times \dfrac{1}{2} \times 6 \times 6 \times \sin 60°$

$= 93.53$

$= 93.5$ cm^2 (correct to 3 sig. fig.)

(b) $x(2x) \sin 110° = 93.53$

$x^2 = \dfrac{93.53}{2 \sin 110°}$

$\therefore x = \sqrt{\dfrac{93.53}{2 \sin 110°}}$

$= 7.05$ (correct to 3 sig. fig.)

Section 7.4

14. In $\triangle ABC$, $b = 9$ cm, $\angle A = 56°$ and $\angle C = 23°$. Find the sides a and c.

Solution

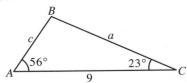

$\angle ABC = 180° - 56° - 23°$ ($\angle$ sum of $\triangle$)

$= 101°$

By the sine rule,

$\dfrac{a}{\sin 56°} = \dfrac{9}{\sin 101°}$

$a = \dfrac{9 \sin 56°}{\sin 101°}$

$= 7.60$ cm (correct to 3 sig. fig.)

By the sine rule,

$\dfrac{c}{\sin 23°} = \dfrac{9}{\sin 101°}$

$c = \dfrac{9 \sin 23°}{\sin 101°}$

$= 3.58$ cm (correct to 3 sig. fig.)

15. In $\triangle ABC$, $b = 10$ cm, $c = 18$ cm and $\angle B = 31°$. Find $\angle A$, $\angle C$ and the side a.

Solution

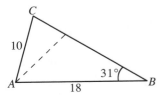

By the sine rule,

$\dfrac{18}{\sin C} = \dfrac{10}{\sin 31°}$

$\sin C = \dfrac{18 \sin 31°}{10}$

$\angle C = 67.98°$ or $180° - 67.98°$

$= 67.98°$ or $112.02°$

$= 68.0°$ or $112.0°$ (correct to 1 d.p.)

When $\angle C = 68.0°$,

$\angle A = 180° - 31° - 68.0°$ ($\angle$ sum of $\triangle$)

$= 81.0°$

$\dfrac{a}{\sin 81.0°} = \dfrac{10}{\sin 31°}$

$a = \dfrac{10 \sin 81.0°}{\sin 31°}$

$= 19.2$ cm (correct to 3 sig. fig.)

When $\angle C = 112.0°$,

$\angle A = 180° - 31° - 112.0°$ ($\angle$ sum of $\triangle$)

$= 37.0°$

$\dfrac{a}{\sin 37.0°} = \dfrac{10}{\sin 31°}$

$a = \dfrac{10 \sin 37.0°}{\sin 31°}$

$= 11.7$ cm (correct to 3 sig. fig.)

$\therefore$ the two possible solutions are:

1. $\angle A = 81.0°$, $\angle C = 68.0°$ and $a = 19.2$ cm;

or

2. $\angle A = 37.0°$, $\angle C = 112.0°$ and $a = 11.7$ cm.

16. In $\triangle PQR$, $p = 12$ cm, $q = 10$ cm and $\angle P = 38°$. Find $\angle Q$, $\angle R$ and the side r.

Solution

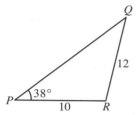

By the sine rule,

$$\frac{10}{\sin Q} = \frac{12}{\sin 38°}$$

$$\sin Q = \frac{10 \sin 38°}{12}$$

$\angle Q = 30.9°$ or $180° - 30.9°$ (correct to 1 d.p.)
$ = 30.9°$ or $149.1°$ (rejected)

$\therefore \quad \angle Q = 30.9°$
$ \angle R = 180° - 38° - 30.9°$
$ = 111.1°$

By the sine rule,

$$\frac{r}{\sin 111.1°} = \frac{12}{\sin 38°}$$

$$r = \frac{12 \sin 111.1°}{\sin 38°}$$

$ = 18.2$ cm (correct to 3 sig. fig.)

$\therefore$ the solution is: $\angle Q = 30.9°$, $\angle R = 111.1°$ and $r = 18.2$ cm.

17. In the diagram, P and Q are two points, 420 m apart, on the ground. H is a helicopter above a point R on the ground. $\angle HPR = 37°$, $\angle HQR = 60°$ and $\angle PRH = 90°$.

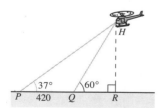

Find
(a) the distance HQ,
(b) the height of the helicopter above the ground.

Solution

(a) $\angle PHQ = 60° - 37°$ (ext. $\angle$ of $\triangle$)
$ = 23°$

By the sine rule, in $\triangle PHQ$,

$$\frac{HQ}{\sin 37°} = \frac{420}{\sin 23°}$$

$$HQ = \frac{420 \sin 37°}{\sin 23°}$$

$ = 646.9$
$ = 647$ m (correct to 3 sig. fig.)

(b) In $\triangle HQR$,

$$\sin 60° = \frac{HR}{HQ}$$

$$HR = 646.9 \times \sin 60°$$

$ = 560$ m (correct to 3 sig. fig.)

$\therefore$ the height of the helicopter above the ground is 560 m.

Section 7.5

18. In $\triangle ABC$, $b = 12$ cm, $c = 18$ cm and $\angle A = 49°$. Find the side a, $\angle B$ and $\angle C$.

Solution

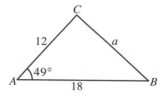

By the cosine rule,
$a^2 = 12^2 + 18^2 - 2 \times 12 \times 18 \times \cos 49°$
$ = 184.58$ cm^2

$a = \sqrt{184.58}$
$ = 13.586$
$ = 13.6$ cm (correct to 3 sig. fig.)

By the sine rule,

$$\frac{12}{\sin B} = \frac{13.586}{\sin 49°}$$

$$\sin B = \frac{12 \sin 49°}{13.586}$$

$\angle B = 41.8°$ (correct to 1 d.p.)
$\angle C = 180° - 41.8° - 49°$
$ = 89.2°$

$\therefore$ the solution is: $a = 13.6$ cm, $\angle B = 41.8°$ and $\angle C = 89.2°$.

7

19. In the diagram, *PQRS* is a parallelogram with *PQ* = 5 cm, *PS* = 3 cm and ∠*QPS* = 105°. Find the length of the diagonal
(a) *QS*,
(b) *PR*.

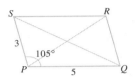

Solution
(a) By the cosine rule,
$$QS^2 = 5^2 + 3^2 - 2 \times 3 \times 5 \times \cos 105°$$
$$= 41.765 \text{ cm}^2$$
$$QS = \sqrt{41.765}$$
$$= 6.46 \text{ cm} \quad \text{(correct to 3 sig. fig.)}$$

(b) In △*PQR*,
∠*PQR* = 180° − 105° (int. ∠s, *PS* // *QR*)
= 75°
RQ = *PS* (opp. sides of // gram)
= 3 cm
By the cosine rule,
$$PR^2 = 5^2 + 3^2 - 2 \times 5 \times 3 \times \cos 75°$$
$$= 26.235$$
$$PR = \sqrt{26.235}$$
$$= 5.12 \text{ cm} \quad \text{(correct to 3 sig. fig.)}$$

20. In △*ABC*, *a* = 10 cm, *b* = 9 cm and *c* = 14 cm. Find the angles of △*ABC*.

Solution

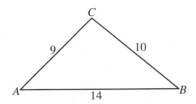

By the cosine rule,
$$\cos C = \frac{9^2 + 10^2 - 14^2}{2 \times 9 \times 10}$$
$$= -0.083\,33$$
∠*C* = 94.78°
= 94.8° (correct to 1 d.p.)
By the sine rule,
$$\frac{10}{\sin A} = \frac{14}{\sin 94.78°}$$
$$\sin A = \frac{10 \sin 94.78°}{14}$$
∠*A* = 45.38°
= 45.4° (correct to 1 d.p.)
∴ ∠*B* = 180° − 45.38° − 94.78°
= 39.84°
= 39.8° (correct to 3 sig. fig.)
∴ the solution is: ∠*A* = 45.4°, ∠*B* = 39.8° and ∠*C* = 94.8°.

Exercise 7.1
Basic Practice

1. State the values of sin A, cos A and tan A in each of the following figures.

(a)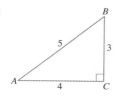

(b)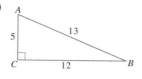

(c)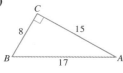

(d)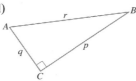

Solution

(a) $\sin A = \dfrac{3}{5}$

$\cos A = \dfrac{4}{5}$

$\tan A = \dfrac{3}{4}$

(b) $\sin A = \dfrac{12}{13}$

$\cos A = \dfrac{5}{13}$

$\tan A = \dfrac{12}{5}$

(c) $\sin A = \dfrac{8}{17}$

$\cos A = \dfrac{15}{17}$

$\tan A = \dfrac{8}{15}$

(d) $\sin A = \dfrac{p}{r}$

$\cos A = \dfrac{q}{r}$

$\tan A = \dfrac{p}{q}$

2. Find the values of the following, giving your answers correct to 4 significant figures.

Solution
(a) $\sin 57° = 0.8367$ (correct to 4 sig. fig.)
(b) $\cos 32.8° = 0.8406$ (correct to 4 sig. fig.)
(c) $\tan 10.9° = 0.1926$ (correct to 4 sig. fig.)
(d) $13 \sin 62.5° = 11.53$ (correct to 4 sig. fig.)
(e) $\cos 20° + \cos 40° = 1.706$ (correct to 4 sig. fig.)
(f) $\sin 66° \times \cos 66° \times \tan 66° = 0.8346$

(correct to 4 sig. fig.)

3. Find the acute angle θ, in degrees, in each of the following.

Solution
(a) $\sin \theta = 0.5$
$\theta = 30°$
(b) $\cos \theta = 0.875$
$\theta = 29.0°$ (correct to 1 d.p.)
(c) $\tan \theta = 1.089$
$\theta = 47.4°$ (correct to 1 d.p.)

(d) $\sin \theta = 1.234$
There is no solution for θ.
(e) $\cos \theta = 2 \times \cos 70°$
$\theta = 46.8°$ (correct to 1 d.p.)
(f) $\tan \theta = \sin 85° \times \cos 17.3°$
$\theta = 43.6°$ (correct to 1 d.p.)

4. Find the value of x in each of the following diagrams.

(a)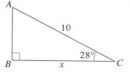

(b)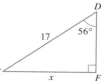

(c)

(d)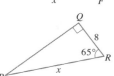

(e)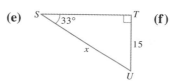

(f)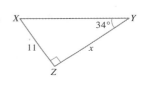

Solution
(a) $\cos 28° = \dfrac{x}{10}$
$x = 10 \cos 28°$
$= 8.83$ (correct to 3 sig. fig.)

(b) $\sin 56° = \dfrac{x}{17}$
$x = 17 \sin 56°$
$= 14.1$ (correct to 3 sig. fig.)

(c) $\tan 30° = \dfrac{x}{25}$
$x = 25 \tan 30°$
$= 14.4$ (correct to 3 sig. fig.)

(d) $\cos 65° = \dfrac{8}{x}$
$x = \dfrac{8}{\cos 65°}$
$= 18.9$ (correct to 3 sig. fig.)

(e) $\sin 33° = \dfrac{15}{x}$
$x = \dfrac{15}{\sin 33°}$
$= 27.5$ (correct to 3 sig. fig.)

(f) $\tan 34° = \dfrac{11}{x}$
$x = \dfrac{11}{\tan 34°}$
$= 16.3$ (correct to 3 sig. fig.)

5. Find the values of x and y in each of the following diagrams.

(a)

(b)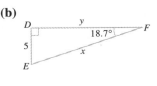

(c)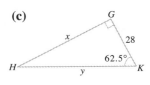

(d)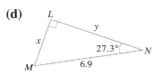

Solution

(a) $\sin 57.2° = \dfrac{x}{14}$

$\qquad x = 14 \sin 57.2°$

$\qquad\quad = 11.8 \quad$ (correct to 3 sig. fig.)

$\cos 57.2° = \dfrac{y}{14}$

$\qquad y = 14 \cos 57.2°$

$\qquad\quad = 7.58 \quad$ (correct to 3 sig. fig.)

(b) $\sin 18.7° = \dfrac{5}{x}$

$\qquad x = \dfrac{5}{\sin 18.7°}$

$\qquad\quad = 15.6 \quad$ (correct to 3 sig. fig.)

$\tan 18.7° = \dfrac{5}{y}$

$\qquad y = \dfrac{5}{\tan 18.7°}$

$\qquad\quad = 14.8 \quad$ (correct to 3 sig. fig.)

(c) $\tan 62.5° = \dfrac{x}{28}$

$\qquad x = 28 \tan 62.5°$

$\qquad\quad = 53.8 \quad$ (correct to 3 sig. fig.)

$\cos 62.5° = \dfrac{28}{y}$

$\qquad y = \dfrac{28}{\cos 62.5°}$

$\qquad\quad = 60.6 \quad$ (correct to 3 sig. fig.)

(d) $\sin 27.3° = \dfrac{x}{6.9}$

$\qquad x = 6.9 \sin 27.3°$

$\qquad\quad = 3.16 \quad$ (correct to 3 sig. fig.)

$\cos 27.3° = \dfrac{y}{6.9}$

$\qquad y = 6.9 \cos 27.3°$

$\qquad\quad = 6.13 \quad$ (correct to 3 sig. fig.)

6. Find the value of the angle θ, in degrees, in each of the following.

(a)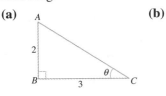

(b)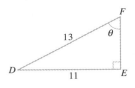

(c)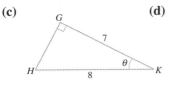

(d)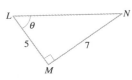

(e)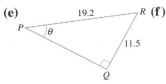

(f)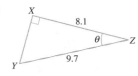

Solution

(a) $\tan \theta = \dfrac{2}{3}$

$\qquad \theta = 33.7° \quad$ (correct to 1 d.p.)

(b) $\sin \theta = \dfrac{11}{13}$

$\qquad \theta = 57.8° \quad$ (correct to 1 d.p.)

(c) $\cos \theta = \dfrac{7}{8}$

$\qquad \theta = 29.0° \quad$ (correct to 1 d.p.)

(d) $\tan \theta = \dfrac{7}{5}$

$\qquad \theta = 54.5° \quad$ (correct to 1 d.p.)

(e) $\sin \theta = \dfrac{11.5}{19.2}$

$\qquad \theta = 36.8° \quad$ (correct to 1 d.p.)

(f) $\cos \theta = \dfrac{8.1}{9.7}$

$\qquad \theta = 33.4° \quad$ (correct to 1 d.p.)

Further Practice

7. In each of the following diagrams, the unit of length is cm. Find the unknown marked sides and angles.

(a)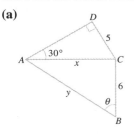

(b)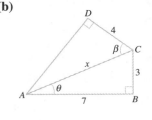

(c) 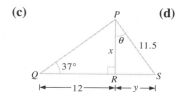 **(d)**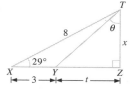

Solution

(a) In $\triangle ACD$,

$$\sin 30° = \frac{5}{x}$$
$$x = \frac{5}{\sin 30°}$$
$$= 10$$
$$\therefore AC = 10 \text{ cm}$$

In $\triangle ABC$,

$$\tan \theta = \frac{x}{6}$$
$$= \frac{10}{6}$$
$$\theta = 59.04°$$
$$= 59.0° \quad \text{(correct to 1 d.p.)}$$

$$\cos \theta = \frac{6}{y}$$
$$y = \frac{6}{\cos 59.04°}$$
$$= 11.7 \quad \text{(correct to 3 sig. fig.)}$$
$$\therefore AB = 11.7 \text{ cm}$$

(b) In $\triangle ABC$,

$$\tan \theta = \frac{3}{7}$$
$$\theta = 23.20°$$
$$= 23.2° \quad \text{(correct to 1 d.p.)}$$

$$\sin \theta = \frac{3}{x}$$
$$x = \frac{3}{\sin 23.20°}$$
$$= 7.615$$
$$= 7.62 \quad \text{(correct to 3 sig. fig.)}$$
$$\therefore AC = 7.62 \text{ cm}$$

In $\triangle ACD$,

$$\cos \beta = \frac{4}{x}$$
$$= \frac{4}{7.615}$$
$$\beta = 58.3° \quad \text{(correct to 1 d.p.)}$$

(c) In $\triangle PQR$,

$$\tan 37° = \frac{x}{12}$$
$$x = 12 \tan 37°$$
$$= 9.0426$$
$$= 9.04 \quad \text{(correct to 3 sig. fig.)}$$
$$\therefore PR = 9.04 \text{ cm}$$

In $\triangle PRS$,

$$\cos \theta = \frac{x}{11.5}$$
$$= \frac{9.0426}{11.5}$$
$$\theta = 38.16°$$
$$= 38.2° \quad \text{(correct to 1 d.p.)}$$

$$\sin \theta = \frac{y}{11.5}$$
$$y = 11.5 \sin 38.16°$$
$$= 7.11 \quad \text{(correct to 3 sig. fig.)}$$
$$\therefore RS = 7.11 \text{ cm}$$

(d) In $\triangle TXZ$,

$$\sin 29° = \frac{x}{8}$$
$$x = 8 \sin 29°$$
$$= 3.8785$$
$$= 3.88 \quad \text{(correct to 3 sig. fig.)}$$
$$\therefore TZ = 3.88 \text{ cm}$$

$$\cos 29° = \frac{3 + t}{8}$$
$$3 + t = 8 \cos 29°$$
$$t = 8 \cos 29° - 3$$
$$= 3.9970$$
$$\therefore YZ = 4.00 \text{ cm} \quad \text{(correct to 3 sig. fig.)}$$

In $\triangle TYZ$,

$$\tan \theta = \frac{t}{x}$$
$$= \frac{3.9970}{3.8785}$$
$$\theta = 45.9° \quad \text{(correct to 1 d.p.)}$$

8. In $\triangle ABC$, $AB = AC = 6$ cm and $BC = 5$ cm. Find
(a) $\angle BAC$,
(b) the perpendicular distance from A to BC.

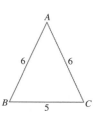

Solution

(a) Draw a perpendicular AN from A to BC.

Then $BN = NC = \frac{1}{2} \times 5 = 2.5$ cm.

In $\triangle ABN$,

$$\sin \angle BAN = \frac{2.5}{6}$$
$$\angle BAN = 24.624°$$
$$\angle BAC = 2\angle BAN$$
$$= 2 \times 24.624°$$
$$= 49.248°$$
$$= 49.2° \quad \text{(correct to 1 d.p.)}$$

(b) $$\cos \angle BAN = \frac{AN}{AB}$$
$$AN = 6 \cos 24.624°$$
$$= 5.45 \text{ cm} \quad \text{(correct to 3 sig. fig.)}$$
$\therefore$ the perpendicular distance from A to BC is 5.45 cm.

9. In the diagram, $ABCD$ is a trapezium, $AB = 8$ cm, $CD = 3$ cm and $AD = 4$ cm. Find

(a) $\angle ABC$,

(b) the length of BC.

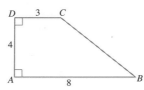

Solution

(a) Draw a perpendicular CN from C to AB.

$$BN = 8 - 3$$
$$= 5 \text{ cm}$$
$$CN = AD$$
$$= 4 \text{ cm}$$

In $\triangle BCN$,

$$\tan \angle ABC = \frac{CN}{BN}$$
$$= \frac{4}{5}$$
$$\angle ABC = 38.66°$$
$$= 38.7° \quad \text{(correct to 1 d.p.)}$$

(b) $\cos \angle ABC = \frac{BN}{BC}$

$$BC = \frac{5}{\cos 38.66°}$$
$$= 6.40 \text{ cm} \quad \text{(correct to 3 sig. fig.)}$$

10. In the diagram, $AD = 9$ cm, $DC = 8$ cm, $\angle ABC = 90°$, $\angle DAB = 25°$ and $\angle BCD = 40°$. Find

(a) the length of AB,

(b) the length of BC,

(c) $\angle CAD$.

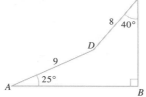

Solution

(a)

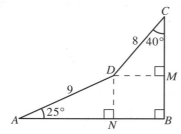

In $\triangle ADN$,

$$\cos 25° = \frac{AN}{9}$$
$$AN = 9 \cos 25°$$
$$= 8.1568$$

In $\triangle CDM$,

$$\sin 40° = \frac{DM}{CD}$$
$$DM = 8 \sin 40°$$
$$= 5.1423$$
$$\therefore \quad AB = AN + DM$$
$$= 8.1568 + 5.1423$$
$$= 13.2991$$
$$= 13.3 \text{ cm} \quad \text{(correct to 3 sig. fig.)}$$

(b) In $\triangle ADN$,

$$\sin 25° = \frac{DN}{AD}$$
$$DN = 9 \sin 25°$$
$$= 3.8036$$

In $\triangle CDM$,

$$\cos 40° = \frac{CM}{CD}$$
$$CM = 8 \cos 40°$$
$$= 6.1284$$
$$\therefore \quad BC = DN + CM$$
$$= 3.8036 + 6.1284$$
$$= 9.932$$
$$= 9.93 \text{ cm} \quad \text{(correct to 3 sig. fig.)}$$

(c) In $\triangle ABC$,

$$\tan \angle BAC = \frac{BC}{AB}$$
$$= \frac{9.932}{13.2991}$$
$$\angle BAC = 36.753°$$
$$\therefore \quad \angle CAD = 36.753° - 25°$$
$$= 11.753°$$
$$= 11.8° \quad \text{(correct to 1 d.p.)}$$

Maths@Work

11. The diagram shows a rectangle $ABCD$ in which $AB = 16$ cm and $BC = 9$ cm. Find

(a) the angle θ,

(b) the length of AC,

(c) the angle α.

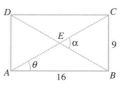

Solution

(a) In $\triangle ABC$,

$$\tan \theta = \frac{9}{16}$$
$$\theta = 29.358°$$
$$\therefore \quad \theta = 29.4° \quad \text{(correct to 1 d.p.)}$$

(b) $\cos \theta = \frac{16}{AC}$

$$AC = \frac{16}{\cos 29.358°}$$
$$= 18.4 \text{ cm} \quad \text{(correct to 3 sig. fig.)}$$

(c) $\angle EBA = \theta$ (base $\angle$s of isos. $\triangle$)
$$= 29.358°$$
$$\alpha = \theta + \angle EBA \quad \text{(ext. } \angle \text{ of } \triangle)$$
$$= 29.358° + 29.358°$$
$$= 58.716°$$
$$\therefore \quad \alpha = 58.7° \quad \text{(correct to 1 d.p.)}$$

12. The diagram shows a rhombus *ABCD* in which *AD* = 15 cm and $\angle BAD = 76°$. Find

(a) the length of *AC*,

(b) the length of *BD*.

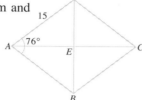

Solution

(a) $\angle EAD = \frac{1}{2} \times 76°$ (diagonal of rhombus)
$$= 38°$$
In $\triangle ADE$,
$$\cos 38° = \frac{AE}{15}$$
$$AE = 15 \cos 38°$$
$$AC = 2AE \quad \text{(diagonal of rhombus)}$$
$$= 2 \times 15 \cos 38°$$
$$= 23.6 \text{ cm} \quad \text{(correct to 3 sig. fig.)}$$

(b) In $\triangle ADE$,
$$\sin 38° = \frac{DE}{15}$$
$$DE = 15 \sin 38°$$
$$BD = 2DE \quad \text{(diagonal of rhombus)}$$
$$= 2 \times 15 \sin 38°$$
$$= 18.5 \text{ cm} \quad \text{(correct to 3 sig. fig.)}$$

13. In the diagram, *TA* and *TB* are tangents to the circle, centre *O*, at *A* and *B* respectively. The radius of the circle is 5 cm and *AB* is 9 cm. Find

(a) $\angle AOB$,

(b) the perpendicular distance from *O* to *AB*,

(c) the length of the tangent *TA*.

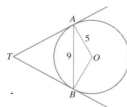

Solution

(a) Join *O* and *T* to cut *AB* at *N*.
Then $ON \perp AB$ and
$$AN = \frac{1}{2} AB$$
$$= 4.5 \text{ cm}$$

In $\triangle OAN$,
$$\sin \angle AON = \frac{4.5}{5}$$
$$\angle AON = 64.158°$$
$$\therefore \quad \angle AOB = 2\angle AON$$
$$= 2 \times 64.158°$$
$$= 128.316°$$
$$= 128.3° \quad \text{(correct to 1 d.p.)}$$

(b) $\cos \angle AON = \frac{ON}{5}$
$$ON = 5 \cos 64.158°$$
$$= 2.18 \text{ cm} \quad \text{(correct to 3 sig. fig.)}$$
i.e. the perpendicular distance from *O* to *AB* is 2.18 cm.

(c) In $\triangle AOT$,
$$\angle OAT = 90° \quad \text{(tangent} \perp \text{radius)}$$
$$\tan \angle AON = \frac{AT}{5}$$
$$AT = 5 \tan 64.158°$$
$$= 10.3 \text{ cm} \quad \text{(correct to 3 sig. fig.)}$$
$\therefore$ length of the tangent *TA* is 10.3 cm.

14. In the diagram, *ABC* is a semicircle with centre *O*, and *TB* is a tangent to the semicircle at *B*. *OB* = 7 cm and $\angle CAB = 38°$.

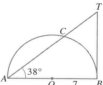

Find

(a) the length of the chord *AC*,

(b) the length of the tangent *TB*,

(c) the length of *CT*,

(d) the perpendicular distance from *O* to the chord *AC*.

Solution

(a) Join *B* and *C*.
$$\angle ACB = 90° \quad (\angle \text{ in a semicircle)}$$
$$AB = 2 \times 7 \quad \text{(diameter of circle)}$$
$$= 14 \text{ cm}$$
In $\triangle ABC$,
$$\cos 38° = \frac{AC}{AB}$$
$$\therefore \quad AC = 14 \cos 38°$$
$$= 11.032$$
$$= 11.0 \text{ cm} \quad \text{(correct to 3 sig. fig.)}$$

(b) In $\triangle ABT$,
$$\angle ABT = 90° \quad \text{(tangent} \perp \text{radius)}$$
$$\tan 38° = \frac{TB}{AB}$$
$$TB = 14 \tan 38°$$
$$= 10.9 \text{ cm} \quad \text{(correct to 3 sig. fig.)}$$

(c) In $\triangle ABT$,

$$\cos 38° = \frac{AB}{AT}$$

$$AT = \frac{14}{\cos 38°}$$

$$= 17.766 \text{ cm}$$

$$\therefore \quad CT = AT - AC$$

$$= 17.766 - 11.032$$

$$= 6.734$$

$$= 6.73 \text{ cm} \quad \text{(correct to 3 sig. fig.)}$$

(d) Draw a perpendicular ON from O to AC.

In $\triangle AON$,

$$\sin 38° = \frac{ON}{7}$$

$$ON = 7 \sin 38°$$

$$= 4.31 \text{ cm} \quad \text{(correct to 3 sig. fig.)}$$

$\therefore$ the required distance is 4.31 cm.

15. AB is a ladder leaning against a vertical wall BF. AB makes an angle of 60° with the horizontal ground and its lower end A is 2 m away from the foot F of the wall. CD represents a new position of the ladder when the upper end B slides down 1 m to D. Find

(a) the length of the ladder,

(b) the height of B above the ground,

(c) the angle that CD makes with the ground.

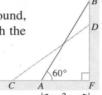

Solution

(a) In $\triangle ABE$,

$$\cos 60° = \frac{2}{AB}$$

$$AB = \frac{2}{\cos 60°}$$

$$= 4 \text{ m}$$

(b) $\tan 60° = \dfrac{BF}{2}$

$$BF = 2 \tan 60°$$

$$= 3.464 \text{ m}$$

$$= 3.46 \text{ m} \quad \text{(correct to 3 sig. fig.)}$$

$\therefore$ B is 3.46 m above the ground.

(c) In $\triangle CDF$,

$$DF = 3.464 - 1$$

$$= 2.464 \text{ cm}$$

$$\sin \angle DCF = \frac{DF}{CD}$$

$$= \frac{2.464}{4}$$

$$\angle DCF = 38.0° \quad \text{(correct to 1 d.p.)}$$

$\therefore$ CD makes an angle of 38.0° with the ground.

16. A surveyor wants to measure the width AC of a river as shown in the diagram. He observes that the river banks are parallel to each other. He walks 27 m from C to B and finds that $\angle ABC = 43.5°$.

(a) Find the width AC.

(b) D is a point along BC produced and is 19 m from C. Find

(i) $\angle CDA$, **(ii)** the distance AD.

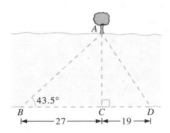

Solution

(a) In $\triangle ABC$,

$$\tan 43.5° = \frac{AC}{BC}$$

$$\therefore \quad AC = 27 \tan 43.5°$$

$$= 25.622$$

$$= 25.6 \text{ m} \quad \text{(correct to 3 sig. fig.)}$$

(b) (i) In $\triangle ACD$,

$$\tan \angle CDA = \frac{AC}{CD}$$

$$= \frac{25.622}{19}$$

$$\angle CDA = 53.44°$$

$$= 53.4° \quad \text{(correct to 1 d.p.)}$$

(ii) $\cos \angle CDA = \dfrac{CD}{AD}$

$$\therefore \quad AD = \frac{19}{\cos 53.44°}$$

$$= 31.9 \text{ m} \quad \text{(correct to 3 sig. fig.)}$$

Brainworks

17. (a) Copy and complete the following table, giving the values correct to 3 decimal places.

θ	5°	20°	40°	60°	80°	85°
$\sin \theta$	0.087	0.342	0.643	0.866	0.985	0.996
$\cos \theta$	0.996	0.940	0.766	0.5	0.174	0.087
$\tan \theta$	0.087	0.364	0.839	1.732	5.671	11.430

(b) Describe how $\sin \theta$, $\cos \theta$ and $\tan \theta$ vary as the angle θ increases from 0° to 90°.

Solution
(b) As the angle θ increases from $0°$ to $90°$,
1. $\sin \theta$ increases from 0 to 1;
2. $\cos \theta$ decreases from 1 to 0;
3. $\tan \theta$ increases from 0 to infinity.

Exercise 7.2
Basic Practice

1. Construct the following angles on a coordinate plane and hence find the values of the sine and cosine of the angles.
   (a) $36°$
   (b) $125°$

Solution

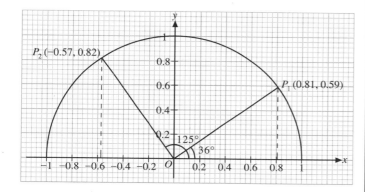

(a) The coordinates of P_1 are $(0.81, 0.59)$.
   $\therefore \sin 36° = 0.59$
   $\cos 36° = 0.81$

(b) The coordinates of P_2 are $(-0.57, 0.82)$.
   $\therefore \sin 125° = 0.82$
   $\cos 125° = -0.57$

2. Express the following in terms of trigonometric ratios of acute angles, without finding their values.

Solution
(a) $\sin 126° = \sin (180° - 54°)$
   $= \sin 54°$

(b) $\cos 154° = \cos (180° - 26°)$
   $= -\cos 26°$

3. Find the values of the following, giving your answers correct to 4 significant figures.

Solution
(a) $\cos 98° = \cos (180° - 82°)$
   $= -\cos 82°$
   $= -0.1392$ (correct to 4 sig. fig.)
(b) $\sin 115° = \sin (180° - 65°)$
   $= \sin 65°$
   $= 0.9063$ (correct to 4 sig. fig.)
(c) $\sin 120° = \sin (180° - 60°)$
   $= \sin 60°$
   $= 0.8660$ (correct to 4 sig. fig.)
(d) $\cos 172° = \cos (180° - 8°)$
   $= -\cos 8°$
   $= -0.9903$ (correct to 4 sig. fig.)

Further Practice

4. In each of the following, find the possible values of θ for $0° \leqslant \theta \leqslant 180°$.

Solution
(a) $\sin \theta = 0.4$
   $\theta = 23.6°$ or $180° - 23.6°$ (correct to 1 d.p.)
   $= 23.6°$ or $156.4°$
(b) $\cos \theta = -0.925$
   $\theta = 180° - 22.3°$ (correct to 1 d.p.)
   $= 157.7°$
(c) $\cos \theta = -0.061$
   $\theta = 180° - 86.5°$ (correct to 1 d.p.)
   $= 93.5°$
(d) $\sin \theta = 0.8043$
   $\theta = 53.5°$ or $180° - 53.5°$ (correct to 1 d.p.)
   $= 53.5°$ or $126.5°$

5. Determine whether each of the following expressions is positive or negative without using a calculator.
   (a) $\sin 46° + \sin 137°$ **(b)** $\cos 109° + \cos 139°$
   (c) $\sin 126° \times \cos 148°$ **(d)** $\cos 168° \div \sin 122°$

Solution
(a) Since $\sin 46° > 0$ and $\sin 137° > 0$,
   $\therefore \sin 46° + \sin 137° > 0$.
   i.e. the result is positive.
(b) Since $\cos 109° < 0$ and $\cos 139° < 0$,
   $\therefore \cos 109° + \cos 139° < 0$.
   i.e. the result is negative.
(c) Since $\sin 126° > 0$ and $\cos 148° < 0$,
   $\therefore \sin 126° \times \cos 148° < 0$.
   i.e. the result is negative.
(d) Since $\cos 168° < 0$ and $\sin 122° > 0$,
   $\therefore \cos 168° \div \sin 122° < 0$.
   i.e. the result is negative.

7

6. The diagram shows a right-angled isosceles triangle ABC with $AC = BC = 1$ cm.
(a) Find the length of AB.
(b) Find the angle θ.
(c) Find the exact values of the following where applicable.

Solution
(a) $\qquad AB^2 = 1^2 + 1^2$ (Pythagoras' Theorem)
$\qquad \therefore\ AB = \sqrt{2}$
$\qquad\qquad = 1.41$ cm

(b) $\qquad\qquad \angle BAC = \theta$ (base $\angle$s of isos. $\triangle$)
$\qquad \theta + \angle BAC + 90° = 180°$ ($\angle$ sum of $\triangle$)
$\qquad \theta + \theta + 90° = 180°$
$\qquad\qquad \therefore\ \theta = 45°$

(c) (i) $\quad \sin 45° = \dfrac{BC}{AB}$
$\qquad\qquad = \dfrac{1}{\sqrt{2}}$
$\qquad\qquad = 0.707$ (to 3 sig. fig.)

(ii) $\quad \cos 45° = \dfrac{AC}{AB}$
$\qquad\qquad = \dfrac{1}{\sqrt{2}}$
$\qquad\qquad = 0.707$ (to 3 sig. fig.)

(iii) $\quad \tan 45° = \dfrac{BC}{AC}$
$\qquad\qquad = \dfrac{1}{1}$
$\qquad\qquad = 1$

(iv) $\quad \sin 135° = \sin (180° - 45°)$
$\qquad\qquad = \sin 45°$
$\qquad\qquad = \dfrac{1}{\sqrt{2}}$
$\qquad\qquad = 0.707$ (to 3 sig. fig.)

(v) $\quad \cos 135° = \cos (180° - 45°)$
$\qquad\qquad = -\cos 45°$
$\qquad\qquad = -\dfrac{1}{\sqrt{2}}$
$\qquad\qquad = -0.707$ (to 3 sig. fig.)

7.

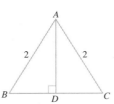

The diagram shows an equilateral triangle ABC with side 2 cm.
(a) Find $\angle ABD$ and $\angle BAD$.
(b) Find the lengths of BD and AD.

(c) Find the values of the following.
(i) $\sin 30°$ (ii) $\cos 30°$
(iii) $\tan 30°$

(d) Find the values of the following.
(i) $\sin 60°$ (ii) $\cos 60°$
(iii) $\tan 60°$

(e) Find the values of the following.
(i) $\sin 120°$ (ii) $\cos 150°$
(iii) $\sin 150°$

Solution
(a) $\quad \angle ABD = 60°$ ($\angle$ of equilateral $\triangle$)
$\qquad \angle BAD = 180° - 60° - 90°$ ($\angle$ sum of $\triangle$)
$\qquad\qquad = 30°$

(b) $\quad BD = \dfrac{1}{2} BC$
$\qquad\qquad = 1$ cm
$\qquad AD^2 = AB^2 - BD^2$ (Pythagoras' theorem)
$\qquad\qquad = 2^2 - 1^2$
$\qquad AD = \sqrt{3}$
$\qquad\qquad = 1.73$ cm (to 3 sig. fig.)

(c) (i) $\quad$ In $\triangle ABD$, $\angle BAD = 30°$.
$\qquad \sin 30° = \dfrac{BD}{AB}$
$\qquad\qquad = \dfrac{1}{2}$

(ii) $\quad \cos 30° = \dfrac{AD}{AB}$
$\qquad\qquad = \dfrac{\sqrt{3}}{2}$
$\qquad\qquad = 0.866$ (to 3 sig. fig.)

(iii) $\quad \tan 30° = \dfrac{BD}{AD}$
$\qquad\qquad = \dfrac{1}{\sqrt{3}}$
$\qquad\qquad = 0.577$ (to 3 sig. fig.)

(d) (i) $\quad$ In $\triangle ABD$, $\angle ABD = 60°$.
$\qquad \sin 60° = \dfrac{AD}{AB}$
$\qquad\qquad = \dfrac{\sqrt{3}}{2}$
$\qquad\qquad = 0.866$ (to 3 sig. fig.)

(ii) $\quad \cos 60° = \dfrac{BD}{AB}$
$\qquad\qquad = \dfrac{1}{2}$

(iii) $\quad \tan 60° = \dfrac{AD}{BD}$
$\qquad\qquad = \dfrac{\sqrt{3}}{1}$
$\qquad\qquad = 1.73$ (to 3 sig. fig.)

(e) (i)
$$\sin 120° = \sin(180° - 60°)$$
$$= \sin 60°$$
$$= \frac{\sqrt{3}}{2}$$
$$= 0.866 \quad \text{(to 3 sig. fig.)}$$

(ii)
$$\cos 150° = \cos(180° - 30°)$$
$$= -\cos 30°$$
$$= -\frac{\sqrt{3}}{2}$$
$$= -0.866 \quad \text{(to 3 sig. fig.)}$$

(iii)
$$\sin 150° = \sin(180° - 30°)$$
$$= \sin 30°$$
$$= \frac{1}{2}$$

Maths@Work

8. In the diagram, AB is a diameter of a circular bicycle track with centre O and radius 40 m. P is the position of a cyclist and $\angle POB = 115°$. Find the perpendicular distance of P from the diameter AB.

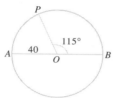

Solution
Draw a perpendicular PN from P to AB.
In $\triangle OPN$,
$$\angle PON = 180° - 115° \quad \text{(adj. } \angle\text{s on a st. line)}$$
$$= 65°$$
$$\sin 65° = \frac{PN}{OP}$$
$$PN = 40 \sin 65°$$
$$= 36.3 \text{ cm} \quad \text{(correct to 3 sig. fig.)}$$
The perpendicular distance of P from the diameter AB is 36.3 cm.

9. In the diagram, a flag is hung on a mast AB that is projected out of a building. $AB = 5$ m, $AF = 12$ m and $\angle FAB = 113°$. Find
(a) the perpendicular distance from B to the vertical wall of the building,
(b) the height of B above the ground.

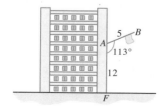

Solution
(a) Draw a perpendicular BN from B to meet FA produced at N.
$$\angle BAN = 180° - 113° \quad \text{(adj. } \angle\text{s on a st. line)}$$
$$= 67°$$
$$\sin 67° = \frac{BN}{AB}$$
$$BN = 5 \sin 67°$$
$$= 4.60 \text{ m} \quad \text{(correct to 3 sig. fig.)}$$
The required distance is 4.60 m.

(b)
$$\cos 67° = \frac{AN}{AB}$$
$$AN = 5 \cos 67°$$
$$= 1.95 \text{ m} \quad \text{(correct to 3 sig. fig.)}$$
Height of B above the ground
$$= 12 + 1.95$$
$$= 13.95 \text{ m}$$
$$= 14.0 \text{ m} \quad \text{(correct to 3 sig. fig.)}$$

10. The diagram shows a lever AB lifting a load. $AB = 20$ m and $BC = 6$ m. Find the angle θ.

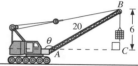

Solution
In $\triangle ABC$,
$$\sin \angle BAC = \frac{BC}{AB}$$
$$= \frac{6}{20}$$
$$\angle BAC = 17.5° \quad \text{(correct to 1 d.p.)}$$
$$\therefore \quad \theta = 180° - \angle BAC \quad \text{(adj. } \angle\text{s on a st. line)}$$
$$= 180° - 17.5°$$
$$= 162.5°$$

Brainworks

11. Can you extend the definitions of $\sin \theta$ and $\cos \theta$ for reflex angle θ (i.e. $180° < \theta < 360°$)? Examine this and support your explanation with appropriate diagrams.

Solution

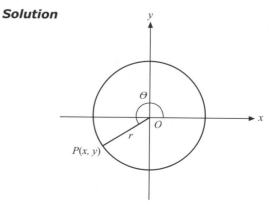

Yes, we can extend the definitions of trigonometric ratios for reflex angle θ. As shown above, we define

$$\sin \theta = \frac{y}{r},$$

and $\qquad \cos \theta = \frac{x}{r}.$

Exercise 7.3
Basic Practice

1. Find the area of each of the following figures. (The unit of length is cm.)

(a)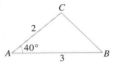

(b)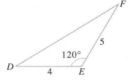

(c)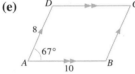

(d)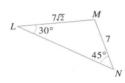

(e)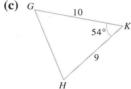

(f)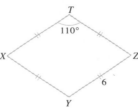

Solution

(a) Area of $\triangle ABC$
$$= \frac{1}{2} \times 2 \times 3 \times \sin 40°$$
$$= 1.93 \text{ cm}^2 \quad \text{(correct to 3 sig. fig.)}$$

(b) Area of $\triangle DEF$
$$= \frac{1}{2} \times 4 \times 5 \times \sin 120°$$
$$= 8.66 \text{ cm}^2 \quad \text{(correct to 3 sig. fig.)}$$

(c) Area of $\triangle GHK$
$$= \frac{1}{2} \times 9 \times 10 \times \sin 54°$$
$$= 36.4 \text{ cm}^2 \quad \text{(correct to 3 sig. fig.)}$$

(d) $\angle LMN = 180° - 30° - 45° \quad (\angle \text{ sum of } \triangle)$
$$= 105°$$
Area of $\triangle LMN$
$$= \frac{1}{2} \times 7\sqrt{2} \times 7 \times \sin 105°$$
$$= 33.5 \text{ cm}^2 \quad \text{(correct to 3 sig. fig.)}$$

(e) Area of parallelogram $ABCD$
$$= 8 \times 10 \times \sin 67°$$
$$= 73.6 \text{ cm}^2 \quad \text{(correct to 3 sig. fig.)}$$

(f) Area of rhombus $TXYZ$
$$= 6 \times 6 \times \sin 110°$$
$$= 33.8 \text{ cm}^2 \quad \text{(correct to 3 sig. fig.)}$$

2. In $\triangle ABC$, $AB = 13$ cm, $AC = 16$ cm and $\angle BAC = 43°$. Find the area of $\triangle ABC$.

Solution

Area of $\triangle ABC = \frac{1}{2} \times 13 \times 16 \times \sin 43°$
$$= 70.9 \text{ cm}^2 \quad \text{(correct to 3 sig. fig.)}$$

3. In $\triangle PQR$, $PQ = 21$ cm, $QR = 15$ cm and $\angle PQR = 109°$. Find the area of $\triangle PQR$.

Solution

Area of $\triangle PQR = \frac{1}{2} \times 21 \times 15 \times \sin 109°$
$$= 149 \text{ cm}^2 \quad \text{(correct to 3 sig. fig.)}$$

4. In a parallelogram $ABCD$, $AB = 12$ cm, $AD = 9$ cm and $\angle ABC = 115°$. Find
(a) the area of $ABCD$,
(b) the perpendicular distance from B to AD.

Solution

(a) Area of $ABCD$
$$= 12 \times 9 \times \sin 115°$$
$$= 97.88$$
$$= 97.9 \text{ cm}^2 \quad \text{(correct to 3 sig. fig.)}$$

(b) Let h cm be the perpendicular distance from B to AD.
Then $\quad AD \times h = $ Area of $ABCD$
$$9 \times h = 97.88$$
$$h = 10.9 \quad \text{(correct to 3 sig. fig.)}$$
$\therefore$ the required distance is 10.9 cm.

5. In the diagram, $ABCD$ is a rhombus, $AD = 7$ cm and $\angle CAD = 31°$. Find
(a) the area of $ABCD$,
(b) the length of AC.

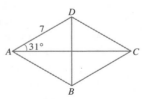

Solution

(a) $\qquad \angle BAC = 31°$ (diagonal of rhombus)
$\therefore \qquad \angle BAD = 31° + 31°$
$$= 62°$$
Area of $ABCD = 7 \times 7 \times \sin 62°$
$$= 43.3 \text{ cm}^2 \quad \text{(correct to 3 sig. fig.)}$$

(b) $\cos 31° = \dfrac{\frac{1}{2} AC}{AD}$
$\therefore \quad AC = 2 \times 7 \cos 31°$
$$= 12.0 \text{ cm} \quad \text{(correct to 3 sig. fig.)}$$

Further Practice

6. In $\triangle ABC$, $BC = 6$ cm, $AB = 4$ cm and the area of $\triangle ABC = 11$ cm^2. Find the possible values of $\angle ABC$.

Solution

$\frac{1}{2} \times 6 \times 4 \times \sin \angle ABC = 11$

$\sin \angle ABC = \frac{11}{12}$

$\angle ABC = 66.4°$ or $180° - 66.4°$ (correct to 1 d.p.)

$\quad\quad\quad = 66.4°$ or $113.6°$

7. In the diagram, $AB = (x + 1)$ cm, $AC = x$ cm and $\angle BAC = 30°$. If the area of $\triangle ABC = 18$ cm^2, find the value of x.

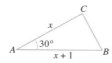

Solution

$\frac{1}{2}x(x + 1)(\sin 30°) = 18$

$\frac{1}{2}(x^2 + x)\left(\frac{1}{2}\right) = 18$

$x^2 + x - 72 = 0$

$(x - 8)(x + 9) = 0$

$\quad\quad x = 8$ or -9 (rejected)

$\therefore \quad\quad x = 8$

8. In the diagram, $ABCD$ is a parallelogram, $AB = 3x$ cm, $AD = 2x$ cm and $\angle BAD = 74°$. If the area of $ABCD$ is 100 cm^2, find the value of x.

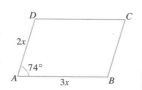

Solution

$(2x)(3x)(\sin 74°) = 100$

$x^2 = \frac{100}{6 \sin 74°}$

$x = \sqrt{\frac{100}{6 \sin 74°}}$

$\quad = 4.16$ (correct to 3 sig. fig.)

9. In the diagram, $AB = CD = 7$ cm, $BD = 8$ cm, $\angle BAD = 90°$ and $\angle BDC = 54°$. Find

(a) the length of AD,

(b) the area of $ABCD$.

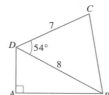

Solution

(a) $AD^2 = 8^2 - 7^2$ (Pythagoras' Theorem)

$AD = \sqrt{15}$

$\quad\quad = 3.87$ cm (correct to 3 sig. fig.)

(b) Area of $ABCD$

$= $ area of $\triangle ABD + $ area of $\triangle BCD$

$= \frac{1}{2} \times 7 \times \sqrt{15} + \frac{1}{2} \times 8 \times 7 \times \sin 54°$

$= 36.2$ cm^2 (correct to 3 sig. fig.)

10. Find the area of a regular octagon inscribed in a circle of radius 10 cm.

Solution

Angle subtended by a side of the octagon at the centre of the circle $= 360° \div 8$

$\quad\quad\quad\quad = 45°$

$\therefore$ area of the octagon

$= 8 \times \frac{1}{2} \times 10 \times 10 \times \sin 45°$

$= 283$ cm^2 (correct to 3 sig. fig.)

11. Find the area of a regular decagon inscribed in a circle of radius 12 cm.

Solution

Angle subtended by a side of the decagon at the centre of the circle $= 360° \div 10$

$\quad\quad\quad\quad = 36°$

$\therefore$ area of the decagon

$= 10 \times \frac{1}{2} \times 12 \times 12 \times \sin 36°$

$= 423$ cm^2 (correct to 3 sig. fig.)

Maths@Work

12. The diagram shows the cross-section of a hut. $AB = 6$ m, $AE = BC = CD = 3$ m, $DE = 4$ m, $\angle EAB = \angle ABC = 90°$, and $\angle CDE = 117°$. Find

(a) the area of the cross-section,

(b) the height of D from AB.

Solution

(a) Area of the cross-section

$= $ area of rectangle $ABCE + $ area of $\triangle CDE$

$= 6 \times 3 + \frac{1}{2} \times 4 \times 3 \times \sin 117°$

$= 23.3$ m^2 (correct to 3 sig. fig.)

(b) Let h m be the height of D from CE. By considering the area of $\triangle CDE$,

$\frac{1}{2} \times 6 \times h = \frac{1}{2} \times 4 \times 3 \times \sin 117°$

$h = 2 \sin 117°$

$\quad = 1.78$ (correct to 3 sig. fig.)

$\therefore$ the height of D from $AB = 3 + 1.78$

$\quad\quad\quad\quad = 4.78$ m

13. The diagram shows a piece of land $ABCD$. $AB = AC = 16$ m, $AD = 13$ m, $\angle BAC = 30°$ and $\angle CAD = 50°$. Find

(a) the perpendicular distance from A to BC,

(b) the area of $ABCD$.

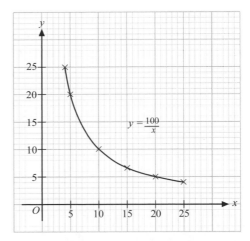

Solution

(a) Draw the perpendicular AN from A to BC.

$$\text{Then} \quad \angle BAN = \frac{1}{2} \times 30°$$
$$= 15°$$
$$\cos 15° = \frac{AN}{AB}$$
$$AN = 16 \cos 15°$$
$$= 15.5 \text{ (correct to 3 sig. fig.)}$$

The required distance is 15.5 m.

(b) Area of $ABCD$
$= $ area of $\triangle ABC + $ area of $\triangle ACD$
$$= \frac{1}{2} \times 16 \times 16 \times \sin 30° + \frac{1}{2} \times 16 \times 13 \times \sin 50°$$
$$= 144 \text{ m}^2 \quad \text{(correct to 3 sig. fig.)}$$

Brainworks

14.

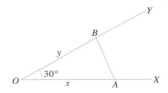

In the diagram, OX and OY are two fixed rays such that $\angle XOY = 30°$. A and B are two variable points on OX and OY respectively, such that the area of $\triangle OAB$ is always 25 cm^2. Let OA be x cm and OB be y cm.

(a) Find the equation connecting x and y.

(b) Draw the graph of y against x for $4 \leqslant x \leqslant 25$.

(c) Describe the variation between x and y.

Solution

(a) $\quad \frac{1}{2}(x)(y)(\sin 30°) = 25$

$$\frac{1}{2}(xy)\left(\frac{1}{2}\right) = 25$$
$$xy = 100$$
$$y = \frac{100}{x}$$

This is the equation connecting x and y.

(b)

x	4	5	10	15	20	25
$y = \dfrac{100}{x}$	25	20	10	6.7	5	4

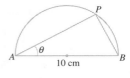

(c) As x increases, y decreases. When x is very large, y is a very small positive number.

15. (a) In the diagram, P is a point on the semicircle with diameter AB of length 10 cm. What is the maximum area of $\triangle ABP$?

(b) Hence find the perimeter of $\triangle ABP$ when its area is maximum.

Solution

(a) $\quad \cos \theta = \frac{AP}{AB}$

$$AP = 10 \cos \theta$$

$$\text{Area of } \triangle ABP = \frac{1}{2} \times 10 \times 10 \cos \theta \times \sin \theta$$
$$= 50 \cos \theta \sin \theta$$

By evaluating the area of $\triangle ABP$ for various values of θ between $0°$ and $90°$ (probably using a spreadsheet program), it can be found that the area is maximum when $\theta = 45°$.

$\therefore$ maximum area of $\triangle ABP$
$$= 50 \cos 45° \sin 45°$$
$$= 25 \text{ cm}^2$$

(b) When $\theta = 45°$, $\quad AP = 10 \cos 45°$
$$= 10 \times \frac{1}{\sqrt{2}}$$
$$= 5\sqrt{2} \text{ cm}$$

and $\qquad\qquad BP = 10 \sin 45°$
$$= 10 \times \frac{1}{\sqrt{2}}$$
$$= 5\sqrt{2} \text{ cm}$$

$\therefore$ perimeter of $\triangle ABP = 10 + 5\sqrt{2} + 5\sqrt{2}$
$$= 24.1 \text{ cm}$$
$$\text{(correct to 3 sig. fig.)}$$

Exercise 7.4
Basic Practice

1. Find the unknown side a in each of the following diagrams. The unit of length is cm.

   (a)
   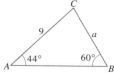

   (b)
   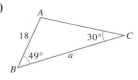

   Solution
   (a) By the sine rule,
   $$\frac{a}{\sin 44°} = \frac{9}{\sin 60°}$$
   $$a = \frac{9 \sin 44°}{\sin 60°}$$
   $$= 7.22 \text{ cm} \quad \text{(correct to 3 sig. fig.)}$$

   (b) $\angle A = 180° - 49° - 30°$ ($\angle$ sum of $\triangle$)
   $$= 101°$$
   By the sine rule,
   $$\frac{a}{\sin 101°} = \frac{18}{\sin 30°}$$
   $$a = \frac{18 \sin 101°}{\sin 30°}$$
   $$= 35.3 \text{ cm} \quad \text{(correct to 3 sig. fig.)}$$

2. Find the unknown angle θ in each of the following diagrams.

   (a)
   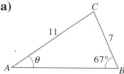

   (b)
   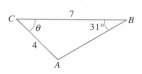

   Solution
   (a) By the sine rule,
   $$\frac{7}{\sin \theta} = \frac{11}{\sin 67°}$$
   $$\sin \theta = \frac{7 \sin 67°}{11}$$
   $$\theta = 35.9° \text{ or } 180° - 35.9° \quad \text{(correct to 1 d.p.)}$$
   $$= 35.9° \text{ or } 144.1° \text{ (rejected)}$$
   $$\therefore \ \theta = 35.9°$$

   (b) By the sine rule,
   $$\frac{7}{\sin A} = \frac{4}{\sin 31°}$$
   $$\sin A = \frac{7 \sin 31°}{4}$$
   $$\angle A = 64.3° \text{ or } 180° - 64.3° \quad \text{(correct to 1 d.p.)}$$
   $$= 64.3° \text{ or } 115.7°$$
   When $\angle A = 64.3°$,
   $$\theta = 180° - 64.3° - 31°$$
   $$= 84.7°$$

   When $\angle A = 115.7°$,
   $$\theta = 180° - 115.7° - 31°$$
   $$= 33.3°$$
   Hence, the solutions are: $\theta = 84.7°$ or $33.3°$.

3. In $\triangle ABC$, $a = 8$ cm, $\angle A = 70°$, $\angle B = 32°$. Find b.

   Solution
   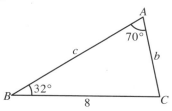

   By the sine rule,
   $$\frac{b}{\sin 32°} = \frac{8}{\sin 70°}$$
   $$b = \frac{8 \sin 32°}{\sin 70°}$$
   $$= 4.51 \text{ cm} \quad \text{(correct to 3 sig. fig.)}$$

4. In $\triangle PQR$, $r = 15$ cm, $\angle P = 27°$, $\angle Q = 105°$. Find q.

   Solution
   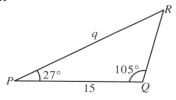

   $$\angle R = 180° - 27° - 105° \quad (\angle \text{ sum of } \triangle)$$
   $$= 48°$$
   By the sine rule,
   $$\frac{q}{\sin 105°} = \frac{15}{\sin 48°}$$
   $$q = \frac{15 \sin 105°}{\sin 48°}$$
   $$= 19.5 \text{ cm} \quad \text{(correct to 3 sig. fig.)}$$

5. In $\triangle ABC$, $b = 5$ cm, $c = 10$ cm, $\angle B = 27°$. Find $\angle C$.

   Solution
   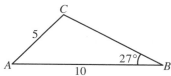

   By the sine rule,
   $$\frac{10}{\sin C} = \frac{5}{\sin 27°}$$
   $$\sin C = 2 \sin 27°$$
   $$\angle C = 65.2° \text{ or } 180° - 65.2° \quad \text{(correct to 1 d.p.)}$$
   $$= 65.2° \text{ or } 114.8°$$

6. In $\triangle XYZ$, $x = 9$ cm, $z = 4$ cm, $\angle X = 130°$. Find $\angle Y$.

Solution

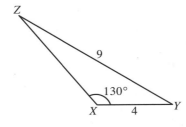

By the sine rule,

$$\frac{4}{\sin Z} = \frac{9}{\sin 130°}$$

$$\sin Z = \frac{4 \sin 130°}{9}$$

$\angle Z = 19.9°$ or $180° - 19.9°$ (correct to 1 d.p.)

$\quad = 19.9°$ or $160.1°$ (rejected)

$\quad = 19.9°$

$\therefore \angle Y = 180° - 130° - 19.9°$

$\quad = 30.1°$

Further Practice

7. In $\triangle ABC$, $b = 16$ cm, $\angle B = 63°$, $\angle C = 41°$. Find $\angle A$, the sides a and c.

Solution

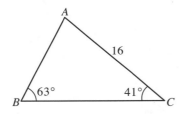

$\angle A = 180° - 63° - 41°$ ($\angle$ sum of $\triangle$)

$\quad = 76°$

By the sine rule,

$$\frac{a}{\sin 76°} = \frac{16}{\sin 63°}$$

$$a = \frac{16 \sin 76°}{\sin 63°}$$

$\quad = 17.4$ cm $\quad$ (correct to 3 sig. fig.)

$$\frac{c}{\sin 41°} = \frac{16}{\sin 63°}$$

$$c = \frac{16 \sin 41°}{\sin 63°}$$

$\quad = 11.8$ cm $\quad$ (correct to 3 sig. fig.)

$\therefore$ the solution is: $\angle A = 76°$, $a = 17.4$ cm and $c = 11.8$ cm.

8. In $\triangle PQR$, $r = 7$ cm, $\angle P = 100°$, $\angle R = 35°$. Find the area of $\triangle PQR$.

Solution

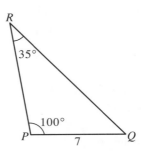

$\angle Q = 180° - 100° - 35°$ ($\angle$ sum of $\triangle$)

$\quad = 45°$

By the sine rule,

$$\frac{q}{\sin 45°} = \frac{7}{\sin 35°}$$

$$q = \frac{7 \sin 45°}{\sin 35°}$$

$\quad = 8.6296$ cm

Area of $\triangle PQR = \frac{1}{2} \times 7 \times 8.6296 \times \sin 100°$

$\quad = 29.7$ cm^2 $\quad$ (correct to 3 sig. fig.)

9. In $\triangle ABC$, $b = 11$ cm, $c = 7.5$ cm and $\angle C = 38°$. Find $\angle A$, $\angle B$ and the side a.

Solution

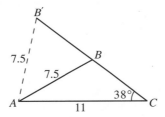

By the sine rule,

$$\frac{11}{\sin B} = \frac{7.5}{\sin 38°}$$

$$\sin B = \frac{11 \sin 38°}{7.5}$$

$\angle B = 64.551°$ or $180° - 64.551°$

$\quad = 64.551°$ or $115.449°$

$\quad = 64.6°$ $\quad$ or $115.4°$ $\quad$ (correct to 1 d.p.)

When $\angle B = 64.551°$,

$\angle A = 180° - 38° - 64.551°$ ($\angle$ sum of $\triangle$)

$\quad = 77.449°$

$\quad = 77.4°$ $\quad\quad\quad\quad$ (correct to 1 d.p.)

By the sine rule,

$$\frac{a}{\sin 77.449°} = \frac{7.5}{\sin 38°}$$

$$a = \frac{7.5 \sin 77.449°}{\sin 38°}$$

$$= 11.9 \text{ cm} \qquad \text{(correct to 3 sig. fig.)}$$

When $\angle B = 115.449°$

$$\angle A = 180° - 38° - 115.449°$$

$$= 26.551°$$

$$= 26.6° \qquad \text{(correct to 1 d.p.)}$$

By the sine rule,

$$\frac{a}{\sin 26.551°} = \frac{7.5}{\sin 38°}$$

$$a = \frac{7.5 \sin 26.551°}{\sin 38°}$$

$$= 5.45 \text{ cm} \quad \text{(correct to 3 sig. fig.)}$$

∴ the two sets of solutions are:

$$\angle A = 77.4°, \angle B = 64.6° \text{ and } a = 11.9 \text{ cm}$$

or $\quad \angle A = 26.6°, \angle B = 115.4° \text{ and } a = 5.45 \text{ cm.}$

10. In $\triangle XYZ$, $y = 6$ cm, $z = 5$ cm and $\angle Y = 41°$. Find the perimeter of $\triangle XYZ$.

Solution

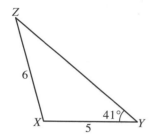

By the sine rule,

$$\frac{5}{\sin Z} = \frac{6}{\sin 41°}$$

$$\sin Z = \frac{5 \sin 41°}{6}$$

$$\angle Z = 33.14° \text{ or } 180° - 33.14°$$

$$= 33.14° \text{ or } 146.86° \text{ (rejected)}$$

∴ $\quad \angle Z = 33.14°$

$$\angle X = 180° - 41° - 33.14°$$

$$= 105.86°$$

By the sine rule,

$$\frac{x}{\sin 105.86°} = \frac{6}{\sin 41°}$$

$$x = \frac{6 \sin 105.86°}{\sin 41°}$$

$$= 8.797 \text{ cm}$$

∴ perimeter of $\triangle XYZ$

$$= 8.797 + 6 + 5$$

$$= 19.797$$

$$= 19.8 \text{ cm} \quad \text{(correct to 3 sig. fig.)}$$

11. In the diagram, $AB = 15$ cm, $\angle ABD = 29°$, $\angle CBD = 47°$ and $\angle BCD = 80°$. Find
    (a) the length of BD,
    (b) the length of CD.

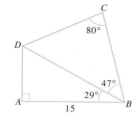

Solution

(a) In $\triangle ABD$,

$$\cos 29° = \frac{AB}{BD}$$

$$BD = \frac{15}{\cos 29°}$$

$$= 17.15$$

$$= 17.2 \text{ cm} \quad \text{(correct to 3 sig. fig.)}$$

(b) In $\triangle BCD$, by the sine rule,

$$\frac{CD}{\sin 47°} = \frac{17.15}{\sin 80°}$$

$$CD = \frac{(17.15) \sin 47°}{\sin 80°}$$

$$= 12.7 \text{ cm} \quad \text{(correct to 3 sig. fig.)}$$

12. In the diagram, $BC = 23$ cm, $\angle ABD = 66°$, $\angle ACB = 42°$ and $AD \perp BC$. Find
    (a) the length of AC,
    (b) the length of AD.

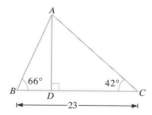

Solution

(a) In $\triangle ABC$,

$$\angle BAC = 180° - 66° - 42° \quad (\angle \text{ sum of } \triangle)$$

$$= 72°$$

By the sine rule,

$$\frac{AC}{\sin 66°} = \frac{23}{\sin 72°}$$

$$AC = \frac{23 \sin 66°}{\sin 72°}$$

$$= 22.093$$

$$= 22.1 \text{ cm} \quad \text{(correct to 3 sig. fig.)}$$

(b) In $\triangle ACD$,

$$\frac{AD}{AC} = \sin 42°$$

∴ $AD = (22.093) \sin 42°$

$$= 14.8 \text{ cm} \quad \text{(correct to 3 sig. fig.)}$$

13. In the diagram, $CD = 9$ cm, $AC = 20$ cm, $\angle ADB = 46°$ and $\angle ABC = 90°$. Find
(a) $\angle ACB$,
(b) the length of AD.

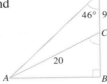

Solution

(a) In $\triangle ACD$, by the sine rule,

$$\frac{9}{\sin \angle CAD} = \frac{20}{\sin 46°}$$

$$\sin \angle CAD = \frac{9 \sin 46°}{20}$$

$$\angle CAD = 18.89° \text{ or } 180° - 18.89°$$
$$= 18.89° \text{ or } 161.11° \text{ (rejected)}$$
$$= 18.89°$$

$$\angle ACB = 46° + 18.89° \quad \text{(ext. } \angle \text{ of } \triangle\text{)}$$
$$= 64.89°$$
$$= 64.9° \quad \text{(correct to 1 d.p.)}$$

(b) $\angle ACD = 180° - 64.89° \quad \text{(adj. } \angle\text{s on a st. line)}$
$$= 115.11°$$

By the sine rule,

$$\frac{AD}{\sin 115.11°} = \frac{20}{\sin 46°}$$

$$AD = \frac{20 \sin 115.11°}{\sin 46°}$$

$$= 25.2 \text{ cm} \quad \text{(correct to 3 sig. fig.)}$$

Maths@Work

14. In an experiment, some masses are hung in equilibrium as shown in the diagram. $AB = 40$ cm, $\angle CAB = 50°$, $\angle CBA = 29°$. Find
(a) the length of AC,
(b) the length of BC,
(c) the perpendicular distance from C to AB.

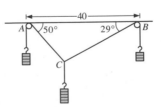

Solution

(a) $\angle ACB = 180° - 50° - 29° \quad (\angle \text{ sum of } \triangle)$
$$= 101°$$

By the sine rule,

$$\frac{AC}{\sin 29°} = \frac{40}{\sin 101°}$$

$$AC = \frac{40 \sin 29°}{\sin 101°}$$

$$= 19.755$$

$$= 19.8 \text{ cm} \quad \text{(correct to 3 sig. fig.)}$$

(b) By the sine rule,

$$\frac{BC}{\sin 50°} = \frac{40}{\sin 101°}$$

$$BC = \frac{40 \sin 50°}{\sin 101°}$$

$$= 31.2 \text{ cm} \quad \text{(correct to 3 sig. fig.)}$$

(c) Draw a perpendicular CN from C to AB.

$$\frac{CN}{AC} = \sin 50°$$

$$CN = (19.755) \sin 50°$$

$$= 15.1 \text{ cm} \quad \text{(correct to 3 sig. fig.)}$$

$\therefore$ the required distance is 15.1 cm.

15. In the diagram, P and Q are two points on horizontal ground and B is a hot-air balloon. $PQ = 260$ m, $\angle BPQ = 31°$ and $\angle BQR = 52°$. Find
(a) the distance PB,
(b) the height of the balloon B above the ground.

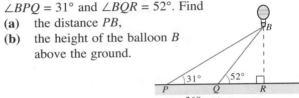

Solution

(a) In $\triangle PBQ$,
$$\angle PBQ = 52° - 31° \quad \text{(ext. } \angle \text{ of } \triangle\text{)}$$
$$= 21°$$
$$\angle PQB = 180° - 52° \quad \text{(adj. } \angle\text{s on a st. line)}$$
$$= 128°$$

By the sine rule,

$$\frac{PB}{\sin 128°} = \frac{260}{\sin 21°}$$

$$PB = \frac{260 \sin 128°}{\sin 21°}$$

$$= 571.71$$

$$= 572 \text{ m} \quad \text{(correct to 3 sig. fig.)}$$

(b) In $\triangle BPR$,

$$\sin 31° = \frac{BR}{PB}$$

$$BR = (571.71) \sin 31°$$

$$= 294 \text{ m} \quad \text{(correct to 3 sig. fig.)}$$

$\therefore$ the required height is 294 m.

16. In the diagram, A and B are two points on the opposite banks of a river. $AB = 237$ m and $\angle BAC = 45°$. A man swims 180 m from B to a point C on the opposite bank. Assume that the river banks are parallel, find
(a) $\angle ACB$,
(b) the distance AC.

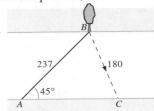

Solution

(a) By the sine rule,

$$\frac{237}{\sin \angle ACB} = \frac{180}{\sin 45°}$$

$$\sin \angle ACB = \frac{237 \sin 45°}{180}$$

$$\angle ACB = 68.59° \quad \text{or} \quad 180° - 68.59°$$
$$= 68.59° \quad \text{or} \quad 111.41°$$
$$= 68.6° \quad \text{or} \quad 111.4° \quad \text{(correct to 1 d.p.)}$$

(b) When $\angle ACB = 68.59°$,
$$\angle ABC = 180° - 45° - 68.59°$$
$$= 66.41°$$
By the sine rule,
$$\frac{AC}{\sin 66.41°} = \frac{180}{\sin 45°}$$
$$AC = \frac{180 \sin 66.41°}{\sin 45°}$$
$$= 233 \text{ m} \quad \text{(correct to 3 sig. fig.)}$$
When $\angle ACB = 111.41°$,
$$\angle ABC = 180° - 45° - 111.41°$$
$$= 23.59°$$
By the sine rule,
$$\frac{AC}{\sin 23.59°} = \frac{180}{\sin 45°}$$
$$AC = \frac{180 \sin 23.59°}{\sin 45°}$$
$$= 102 \text{ m} \quad \text{(correct to 3 sig. fig.)}$$
i.e. the distance AC is 233 m or 102 m.

17. Mr Lim owns a triangular piece of land PQR as shown in the diagram. $PQ = 40$ m, $QR = 26$ m and $\angle QPR = 38°$. Find
(a) the length of PR,
(b) the area of the land.

Solution

(a) In $\triangle PQR$, by the sine rule,
$$\frac{40}{\sin \angle PRQ} = \frac{26}{\sin 38°}$$
$$\sin \angle PRQ = \frac{40 \sin 38°}{26}$$
$$\angle PRQ = 71.29° \quad \text{or} \quad 180° - 71.29°$$
$$= 71.29° \quad \text{or} \quad 108.71°$$
When $\angle PRQ = 71.29°$,
$$\angle PQR = 180° - 38° - 71.29° \quad (\angle \text{ sum of } \triangle)$$
$$= 70.71°$$
By the sine rule,
$$\frac{PR}{\sin 70.71°} = \frac{26}{\sin 38°}$$
$$PR = \frac{26 \sin 70.71°}{\sin 38°}$$
$$= 39.86$$
$$= 39.9 \text{ m} \quad \text{(correct to 3 sig. fig.)}$$

When $\angle PRQ = 108.71°$,
$$\angle PQR = 180° - 38° - 108.71°$$
$$= 33.29°$$
By the sine rule,
$$\frac{PR}{\sin 33.29°} = \frac{26}{\sin 38°}$$
$$PR = \frac{26 \sin 33.29°}{\sin 38°}$$
$$= 23.18$$
$$= 23.2 \text{ m} \quad \text{(correct to 3 sig. fig.)}$$

(b) Area of the land
$$= \left(\frac{1}{2} \times 40 \times 26 \times \sin 70.71°\right) \text{ or}$$
$$\left(\frac{1}{2} \times 40 \times 26 \times \sin 33.29°\right)$$
$$= 491 \text{ m}^2 \text{ or } 285 \text{ m}^2 \quad \text{(correct to 3 sig. fig.)}$$

Brainworks

18. In $\triangle ABC$, $AB = 5$ cm and $\angle BAC = 36°$. Find the possible length(s) of BC such that the number of possible $\triangle ABC$s that can be formed is
(a) 2,
(b) 1,
(c) 0.

Solution

(a)

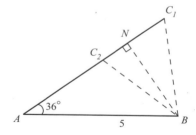

Construct a diagram as shown above.
$$\frac{BN}{AB} = \sin 36°$$
$$BN = 5 \sin 36°$$
$$= 2.94 \text{ cm} \quad \text{(correct to 3 sig. fig.)}$$
There are two possible solutions of $\triangle ABC$ when $2.94 < BC < 5$.
For example, when $BC = 3.2$, we get $\triangle ABC_1$, and $\triangle ABC_2$ as shown.

(b) When $BC = BN = 2.94$ cm, we have only 1 solution of $\triangle ABC$, which is $\triangle ABN$.

(c) When $BC < BN$, there are no solutions of $\triangle ABC$. For example, when $BC = 2$ cm, no triangle can be formed.

Exercise 7.5
Basic Practice

1. Find the unknown side x in each of the following diagrams. The unit of length is cm.

(a)
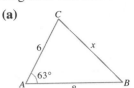

(b)
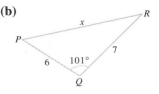

Solution

(a) By the cosine rule,
$$x^2 = 6^2 + 8^2 - 2 \times 6 \times 8 \times \cos 63°$$
$$x = \sqrt{56.4169}$$
$$= 7.51 \quad \text{(correct to 3 sig. fig.)}$$
∴ the unknown side is 7.51 cm.

(b) By the cosine rule,
$$x^2 = 6^2 + 7^2 - 2 \times 6 \times 7 \times \cos 101°$$
$$x = \sqrt{101.03}$$
$$= 10.1 \quad \text{(correct to 3 sig. fig.)}$$
∴ the unknown side is 10.1 cm.

2. Find the unknown angle θ in each of the following diagrams.

(a)
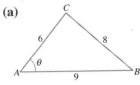

(b)
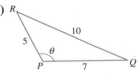

Solution

(a) By the cosine rule,
$$\cos \theta = \frac{6^2 + 9^2 - 8^2}{2 \times 6 \times 9}$$
$$= 0.49074$$
$$\theta = 60.6° \quad \text{(correct to 1 d.p.)}$$

(b) By the cosine rule,
$$\cos \theta = \frac{5^2 + 7^2 - 10^2}{2 \times 5 \times 7}$$
$$= -0.37143$$
$$\theta = 111.8° \quad \text{(correct to 1 d.p.)}$$

3. In $\triangle ABC$, $a = 17$ cm, $b = 13$ cm and $\angle C = 65°$. Find c.

Solution

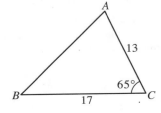

By the cosine rule,
$$c^2 = 13^2 + 17^2 - 2 \times 13 \times 17 \times \cos 65°$$
$$c = \sqrt{271.20}$$
$$= 16.5 \text{ cm} \quad \text{(correct to 3 sig. fig.)}$$

4. In $\triangle PQR$, $q = 9$ cm, $r = 5$ cm and $\angle P = 102°$. Find p.

Solution

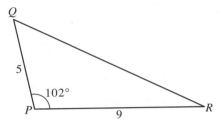

By the cosine rule,
$$p^2 = 5^2 + 9^2 - 2 \times 5 \times 9 \times \cos 102°$$
$$p = \sqrt{124.71}$$
$$= 11.2 \text{ cm} \quad \text{(correct to 3 sig. fig.)}$$

5. In $\triangle ABC$, $a = 6$ cm, $b = 7$ cm and $c = 4$ cm. Find the smallest angle.

Solution

$\angle C$ is the smallest angle.
By the cosine rule,
$$\cos C = \frac{6^2 + 7^2 - 4^2}{2 \times 6 \times 7}$$
$$= 0.8214$$
$$\angle C = 34.8° \quad \text{(correct to 1 d.p.)}$$
i.e. the smallest angle is 34.8°.

6. In $\triangle XYZ$, $x = 9$ cm, $y = 13$ cm and $z = 17$ cm. Find the largest angle.

Solution

$\angle Z$ is the largest angle.
By the cosine rule,
$$\cos Z = \frac{9^2 + 13^2 - 17^2}{2 \times 9 \times 13}$$
$$= -0.16667$$
$$\angle Z = 99.6° \quad \text{(correct to 1 d.p.)}$$
∴ the largest angle is 99.6°.

Further Practice

7. In $\triangle ABC$, $a = 8$ cm, $c = 7$ cm and $\angle B = 50°$. Find the side b, $\angle A$ and $\angle C$.

Solution

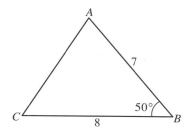

By the cosine rule,
$$b^2 = 8^2 + 7^2 - 2 \times 7 \times 8 \times \cos 50°$$
$$b = \sqrt{41.008}$$
$$= 6.4037$$
$$= 6.40 \text{ cm} \qquad \text{(correct to 3 sig. fig.)}$$
By the sine rule,
$$\frac{7}{\sin C} = \frac{6.4037}{\sin 50°}$$
$$\sin C = \frac{7 \sin 50°}{6.4037}$$
$$\angle C = 56.9° \qquad \text{(correct to 1 d.p.)}$$
$$\therefore \angle A = 180° - 50° - 56.9° \qquad (\angle \text{ sum of } \triangle)$$
$$= 73.1°$$
i.e. the solution is:
$$\angle A = 73.1°, \angle C = 56.9° \text{ and } b = 6.40 \text{ cm.}$$

8. In $\triangle PQR$, $p = 12$ cm, $q = 13$ cm and $r = 5$ cm. Find the angles of $\triangle PQR$.

Solution
By the cosine rule,
$$\cos Q = \frac{5^2 + 12^2 - 13^2}{2 \times 5 \times 12}$$
$$= 0$$
$$\angle Q = 90°$$
$$\sin P = \frac{12}{13}$$
$$\angle P = 67.4° \qquad \text{(correct to 1 d.p.)}$$
$$\therefore \angle R = 180° - 90° - 67.4°$$
$$= 22.6°$$
$$\therefore \text{ the solution is:}$$
$$\angle P = 67.4°, \angle Q = 90° \text{ and } \angle R = 22.6°.$$

9. In the diagram, $ABCD$ is a parallelogram with diagonals AC and BD intersecting at E. $AC = 22$ cm, $BD = 12$ cm and $\angle BEC = 63°$. Find
   (a) the length of BC,
   (b) the length of AB,
   (c) $\angle ABC$.

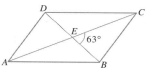

Solution
(a) $CE = \frac{1}{2}AC$ (diagonal of //gram)
$$= \frac{1}{2} \times 22$$
$$= 11 \text{ cm}$$
Similarly,
$$BE = \frac{1}{2} \times 12 = 6 \text{ cm}$$
In $\triangle BCE$, by the cosine rule,
$$BC^2 = 6^2 + 11^2 - 2 \times 6 \times 11 \times \cos 63°$$
$$BC = \sqrt{97.073}$$
$$= 9.8526$$
$$= 9.85 \text{ cm} \qquad \text{(correct to 3 sig. fig.)}$$

(b) In $\triangle ABE$,
$$\angle AEB = 180° - 63° \qquad \text{(adj. } \angle \text{s on a st. line)}$$
$$= 117°.$$
By the cosine rule,
$$AB^2 = 6^2 + 11^2 - 2 \times 6 \times 11 \times \cos 117°$$
$$AB = \sqrt{216.93}$$
$$= 14.729$$
$$= 14.7 \text{ cm} \qquad \text{(correct to 3 sig. fig.)}$$

(c) In $\triangle ABC$, by the cosine rule,
$$\cos \angle ABC = \frac{14.729^2 + 9.8526^2 - 22^2}{2(14.729)(9.8526)}$$
$$= -0.5857$$
$$\angle ABC = 125.9° \qquad \text{(correct to 1 d.p.)}$$

10. In the diagram, M is the midpoint of BC, $AB = 4$ cm, $AC = 5$ cm and $\angle BAC = 123°$. Find
    (a) the length of BC,
    (b) the length of AM.

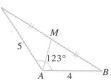

Solution
(a) In $\triangle ABC$, by the cosine rule,
$$BC^2 = 4^2 + 5^2 - 2 \times 4 \times 5 \times \cos 123°$$
$$BC = \sqrt{62.786}$$
$$= 7.9238$$
$$= 7.92 \text{ cm} \qquad \text{(correct to 3 sig. fig.)}$$

(b) By the sine rule,
$$\frac{5}{\sin B} = \frac{7.9238}{\sin 123°}$$
$$\sin B = \frac{5 \sin 123°}{7.9238}$$
$$\angle B = 31.95°$$
In $\triangle ABM$,
$$BM = \frac{1}{2}BC$$
$$= \frac{1}{2} \times 7.9238$$
$$= 3.9619$$

By the cosine rule,
$$AM^2 = 4^2 + 3.9619^2 - 2 \times 4 \times 3.9619$$
$$\times \cos 31.95°$$
$$AM = \sqrt{4.8030}$$
$$= 2.19 \text{ cm} \quad \text{(correct to 3 sig. fig.)}$$

11. In the diagram, $CD \perp AB$, $AB = 9$ cm, $BC = 8$ cm and $AC = 6$ cm. Find

(a) $\angle ABC$,

(b) the length of CD.

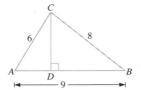

Solution

(a) In $\triangle ABC$, by the cosine rule,
$$\cos \angle ABC = \frac{9^2 + 8^2 - 6^2}{2 \times 9 \times 8}$$
$$\angle ABC = 40.80°$$
$$= 40.8° \quad \text{(correct to 1 d.p.)}$$

(b) In $\triangle BCD$,
$$\sin \angle ABC = \frac{CD}{BC}$$
$$\therefore \quad CD = 8 \sin 40.80°$$
$$= 5.23 \text{ cm} \quad \text{(correct to 3 sig. fig.)}$$

12.

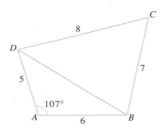

In the diagram, $ABCD$ is a quadrilateral, $AB = 6$ cm, $BC = 7$ cm, $CD = 8$ cm, $DA = 5$ cm and $\angle BAD = 107°$. Find

(a) the length of BD,

(b) $\angle BCD$,

(c) the area of $ABCD$.

Solution

(a) In $\triangle ABD$, by the cosine rule,
$$BD^2 = 5^2 + 6^2 - 2 \times 5 \times 6 \times \cos 107°$$
$$BD = \sqrt{78.5423}$$
$$= 8.8624$$
$$= 8.86 \text{ cm} \quad \text{(correct to 3 sig. fig.)}$$

(b) In $\triangle BCD$, by the cosine rule,
$$\cos \angle BCD = \frac{7^2 + 8^2 - 8.8624^2}{2 \times 7 \times 8}$$
$$= 0.3077$$
$$\angle BCD = 72.08°$$
$$= 72.1° \quad \text{(correct to 1 d.p.)}$$

(c) Area of $ABCD$
= area of $\triangle ABD$ + area of $\triangle BCD$
$$= \frac{1}{2} \times 5 \times 6 \times \sin 107° + \frac{1}{2} \times 8 \times 7 \times \sin 72.08°$$
$$= 41.0 \text{ cm}^2 \quad \text{(correct to 3 sig. fig.)}$$

Maths@Work

13. In the diagram, BC represents a tunnel through a mountain. $AB = 70$ m, $AC = 80$ m and $\angle BAC = 55°$. Find the length of the tunnel.

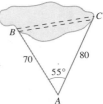

Solution

By the cosine rule,
$$BC^2 = 70^2 + 80^2 - 2 \times 70 \times 80 \times \cos 55°$$
$$BC = \sqrt{4875.94}$$
$$= 69.8 \text{ m} \quad \text{(correct to 3 sig. fig.)}$$
i.e. the length of the tunnel is 69.8 m.

14. In the diagram, L is the position of a police laser gun facing a straight road XY. A car was detected at position A, 120 m from L. Three seconds later, it was detected at position B, 160 m from L. Given that $\angle ALB = 26°$, find

(a) the distance between A and B,

(b) the average speed of the car in km/h when it travelled from A to B.

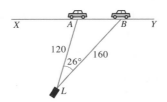

Solution

(a) By the cosine rule,
$$AB^2 = 120^2 + 160^2 - 2 \times 120 \times 160 \times \cos 26°$$
$$AB = \sqrt{5486.31}$$
$$= 74.07 \text{ m}$$
$$= 74.1 \text{ m} \quad \text{(correct to 3 sig. fig.)}$$

(b) Average speed
$$= 74.07 \div 3 \text{ m/s}$$
$$= 24.69 \text{ m/s}$$
$$= 24.69 \times \frac{3600}{1000} \text{ km/h}$$
$$= 88.9 \text{ km/h} \quad \text{(correct to 3 sig. fig.)}$$

15. In the diagram, AB, BC and AC are three straight roads connecting three cities. $AB = 13$ km, $BC = 20$ km and $AC = 17$ km. Find

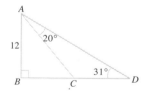

(a) $\angle ABC$,

(b) the shortest distance from A to BC,

(c) the area enclosed by the three roads.

Solution

(a) By the cosine rule,

$$\cos \angle ABC = \frac{13^2 + 20^2 - 17^2}{2 \times 13 \times 20}$$
$$= 0.538\,46$$
$$\angle ABC = 57.42°$$
$$= 57.4° \quad \text{(correct to 1 d.p.)}$$

(b) Draw a perpendicular AN from A to BC.

$$\sin \angle ABC = \frac{AN}{AB}$$
$$\therefore \quad AN = 13 \sin 57.42°$$
$$= 11.0 \text{ km} \quad \text{(correct to 3 sig. fig.)}$$

i.e. the shortest distance from A to BC is 11.0 km.

(c) Area enclosed by the roads
$$= \frac{1}{2} \times 13 \times 20 \times \sin 57.42°$$
$$= 110 \text{ km}^2 \quad \text{(correct to 3 sig. fig.)}$$

Brainworks

16. The diagram shows the junction of Rochor Road and Victoria Street. Suppose both roads intersect at $80°$. At a certain instant, a car P on Rochor Road is 300 m from the junction J, while a car Q on Victoria Street is 400 m from J. What are the two possible distances between P and Q at this instant?

Solution

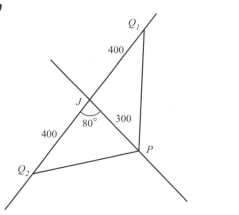

The distance between P and Q may be PQ_1 or PQ_2 as shown in the diagram.

$$\angle PJQ_1 = 180° - 80° \quad \text{(adj. } \angle \text{s on a st. line)}$$
$$= 100°$$

By the cosine rule,
$$PQ_1^2 = 300^2 + 400^2 - 2 \times 300 \times 400 \cos 100°$$
$$PQ_1 = \sqrt{291\,676}$$
$$= 540 \text{ m} \quad \text{(correct to 3 sig. fig.)}$$

and
$$PQ_2^2 = 300^2 + 400^2 - 2 \times 300 \times 400 \times \cos 80°$$
$$PQ_2 = \sqrt{208\,324}$$
$$= 456 \text{ m} \quad \text{(correct to 3 sig. fig.)}$$

$\therefore$ the distance between P and Q is 456 m or 540 m.

17. If we know that the ratio of the three sides of a triangle ABC is $a : b : c = 3 : 5 : 7$, can we find the angles of $\triangle ABC$? If so, what is the largest angle?

Solution

Yes, we can find the angles of $\triangle ABC$.

Let $a = 3k$, $b = 5k$ and $c = 7k$, where k is a positive constant.

Since c is the longest side, $\angle C$ is the largest angle.

By the cosine rule,
$$\cos C = \frac{(3k)^2 + (5k)^2 - (7k)^2}{2(3k)(5k)}$$
$$= \frac{-15k^2}{30k^2}$$
$$= -\frac{1}{2}$$
$$\therefore \quad \angle C = 120°$$

Revision Exercise 7

1. In the diagram, BCD is a straight line, $AB = 12$ cm, $\angle ABC = 90°$, $\angle CAD = 20°$ and $\angle CDA = 31°$. Find

(a) the length of BC,

(b) the length of CD,

(c) the area of $\triangle ACD$.

Solution

(a) $\angle ACB = 20° + 31°$ \quad (ext. $\angle$ of $\triangle$)
$$= 51°$$

In $\triangle ABC$,
$$\tan \angle ACB = \frac{AB}{BC}$$
$$\therefore \quad BC = \frac{12}{\tan 51°}$$
$$= 9.717$$
$$= 9.72 \text{ cm} \quad \text{(correct to 3 sig. fig.)}$$

(b) In △*ABD*,

$$\tan 31° = \frac{12}{BD}$$

$$BD = \frac{12}{\tan 31°}$$

$$= 19.971 \text{ cm}$$

$$∴ \quad CD = BD - BC$$

$$= 19.971 - 9.717$$

$$= 10.254$$

$$= 10.3 \text{ cm} \quad \text{(correct to 3 sig. fig.)}$$

(c) In △*ABC*,

$$\sin 51° = \frac{AB}{AC}$$

$$AC = \frac{12}{\sin 51°}$$

$$= 15.44 \text{ cm}$$

Area of △*ACD*

$$= \frac{1}{2} × 15.44 × 10.254 × \sin (180° - 51°)$$

$$= 61.5 \text{ cm}^2 \quad \text{(correct to 3 sig. fig.)}$$

2. The diagram shows two concentric circles with a common centre *O*, and radii 15 cm and 6 cm respectively. *AC* is a diameter of the large circle. *AB* is a chord of the large circle, as well as a tangent to the small circle at *T*. Find

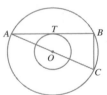

(a) ∠*CAB*,

(b) the length of *AB*,

(c) the area of △*ABC*.

Solution

(a) In △*OAT*,

$$∠OTA = 90° \quad \text{(tangent ⊥ radius)}$$

$$\sin ∠OAT = \frac{OT}{OA}$$

$$= \frac{6}{15}$$

$$∠OAT = 23.58°$$

i.e. ∠*CAB* = 23.6° (correct to 1 d.p.)

(b) $$\cos ∠OAT = \frac{AT}{OA}$$

$$AT = 15 \cos 23.58°$$

$$= 13.7475 \text{ cm}$$

$$∴ \quad AB = 2AT$$

$$= 2 × 13.7475$$

$$= 27.495$$

$$= 27.5 \text{ cm} \quad \text{(correct to 3 sig. fig.)}$$

(c) Area of △*ABC*

$$= \frac{1}{2} × AB × AC × \sin ∠CAB$$

$$= \frac{1}{2} × 27.495 × 30 × \sin 23.58°$$

$$= 165 \text{ cm}^2 \quad \text{(correct to 3 sig. fig.)}$$

3. In the diagram, a regular pentagon *ABCDE* of side 20 cm is inscribed in a circle with centre *O*. Find

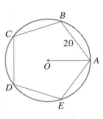

(a) ∠*OAB*,

(b) the length of *OA*,

(c) the area of the pentagon,

(d) the area bounded by the circle and the pentagon.

Solution

(a) Angle sum of a pentagon

$$= (5 - 2) × 180° \quad \text{(∠ sum of polygon)}$$

$$= 540°$$

$$∴ \quad ∠OAB = \frac{1}{2} ∠EAB$$

$$= \frac{1}{2} × \frac{1}{5} × 540°$$

$$= 54°$$

(b) Draw a perpendicular *ON* from *O* to *AB*. Then

$$AN = \frac{1}{2} AB$$

$$= 10 \text{ cm}$$

In △*OAN*,

$$\cos ∠OAN = \frac{AN}{OA}$$

$$OA = \frac{10}{\cos 54°}$$

$$= 17.013$$

$$= 17.0 \text{ cm} \quad \text{(correct to 3 sig. fig.)}$$

(c) Area of the pentagon

$$= 5 × \text{area of } △OAB$$

$$= 5 × \frac{1}{2} × 17.013 × 20 × \sin 54°$$

$$= 688.19$$

$$= 688 \text{ cm}^2 \quad \text{(correct to 3 sig. fig.)}$$

(d) The required area

$$= π × (17.013)^2 - 688.19$$

$$= 221 \text{ cm}^2 \quad \text{(correct to 3 sig. fig.)}$$

4. In the figure, *ABCD* is a parallelogram, *CD* = 8 cm, ∠*BCD* = 62° and ∠*BDC* = 41°. Find

(a) the length of *BC*,

(b) the length of *BD*,

(c) the length of *AC*,

(d) the area of *ABCD*.

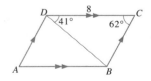

Solution

(a) In △*BCD*,

$$∠CBD = 180° - 41° - 62° \quad \text{(∠ sum of △)}$$

$$= 77°$$

By the sine rule,

$$\frac{BC}{\sin 41°} = \frac{8}{\sin 77°}$$

$$BC = \frac{8 \sin 41°}{\sin 77°}$$

$$= 5.3865$$

$$= 5.39 \text{ cm} \quad \text{(correct to 3 sig. fig.)}$$

(b) By the sine rule,

$$\frac{BD}{\sin 62°} = \frac{8}{\sin 77°}$$

$$BD = \frac{8 \sin 62°}{\sin 77°}$$

$$= 7.2494$$

$$= 7.25 \text{ cm} \quad \text{(correct to 3 sig. fig.)}$$

(c) In $\triangle ABC$,

$$\angle ABC = 180° - 62° \quad \text{(int. } \angle\text{s, } AB \text{ // } DC)$$

$$= 118°$$

By the cosine rule,

$$AC^2 = 8^2 + 5.3865^2 - 2 \times 8 \times 5.3865 \times \cos 118°$$

$$AC = \sqrt{133.475}$$

$$= 11.6 \text{ cm} \quad \text{(correct to 3 sig. fig.)}$$

(d) Area of $ABCD$

$$= 8 \times 5.3865 \times \sin 62°$$

$$= 38.0 \text{ cm}^2 \quad \text{(correct to 3 sig. fig.)}$$

5. In the diagram, $DABE$ is a straight line, BC // EF, $\angle DAC = 136°$, $\angle BEF = 108°$ and $AB = 21$ cm. Find

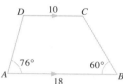

(a) angle β,

(b) angle α,

(c) the length of AC,

(d) the area of $\triangle ABC$.

Solution

(a) $\beta = 180° - 108° \quad \text{(int. } \angle\text{s, } BC \text{ // } EF)$

$$= 72°$$

(b) $\angle ABC = 108° \quad \text{(corr. } \angle\text{s, } BC \text{ // } EF)$

$$\alpha + 108° = 136° \quad \text{(ext. } \angle \text{ of } \triangle)$$

$$\alpha = 28°$$

(c) By the sine rule,

$$\frac{AC}{\sin 108°} = \frac{21}{\sin 28°}$$

$$AC = \frac{21 \sin 108°}{\sin 28°}$$

$$= 42.54$$

$$= 42.5 \text{ cm} \quad \text{(correct to 3 sig. fig.)}$$

(d) $\angle BAC = 180° - 136° \quad \text{(adj. } \angle\text{s on a st. line)}$

$$= 44°$$

Area of $\triangle ABC$

$$= \frac{1}{2} \times 21 \times 42.54 \times \sin 44°$$

$$= 310 \text{ cm}^2 \quad \text{(correct to 3 sig. fig.)}$$

6. In the diagram, $ABCD$ is a trapezium, AB // DC, $AB = 18$ cm, $CD = 10$ cm, $\angle DAB = 76°$ and $\angle ABC = 60°$. Find

(a) the length of BC,

(b) $\angle ACD$,

(c) the length of AD,

(d) the area of $ABCD$.

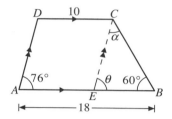

Solution

(a)

Construct CE // AD as shown in the diagram. Then $AECD$ is a parallelogram.

$$AE = CD \quad \text{(opp. sides of //gram)}$$

$$= 10 \text{ cm}$$

In $\triangle BCE$,

$$BE = 18 - 10$$

$$= 8 \text{ cm}$$

$$\theta = 76° \quad \text{(corr. } \angle\text{s, } AD \text{ // } EC)$$

$$\alpha = 180° - 76° - 60° \quad \text{(} \angle \text{ sum of } \triangle)$$

$$= 44°$$

By the sine rule,

$$\frac{BC}{\sin 76°} = \frac{8}{\sin 44°}$$

$$BC = \frac{8 \sin 76°}{\sin 44°}$$

$$= 11.174$$

$$= 11.2 \text{ cm} \quad \text{(correct to 3 sig. fig.)}$$

(b) In $\triangle ABC$, by the cosine rule,

$$AC^2 = 18^2 + 11.174^2 - 2 \times 18 \times 11.174 \times \cos 60°$$

$$AC = \sqrt{247.726}$$

$$= 15.739 \text{ cm}$$

By the sine rule,

$$\frac{11.174}{\sin \angle BAC} = \frac{15.739}{\sin 60°}$$

$$\sin \angle BAC = \frac{11.174 \sin 60°}{15.739}$$

$$\angle BAC = 37.94°$$

$$\angle ACD = \angle BAC \quad \text{(alt. } \angle\text{s, } AB \text{ // } DC)$$

$$= 37.94°$$

$$= 37.9° \quad \text{(correct to 1 d.p.)}$$

(c) In $\triangle BCE$, by the cosine rule,

$$CE^2 = 8^2 + 11.174^2 - 2 \times 8 \times 11.174 \times \cos 60°$$

$$CE = \sqrt{99.466}$$

$$= 9.973$$

$$= 9.97 \text{ cm} \quad \text{(correct to 3 sig. fig.)}$$

$$\therefore AD = CE \quad \text{(opp. } \angle\text{s of //gram)}$$

$$= 9.97 \text{ cm}$$

(d) Area of *ABCD*

= area of parallelogram *AECD* + area of △*BCD*

$= 10 \times 9.973 \times \sin 76° + \frac{1}{2} \times 8 \times 11.174$
$\times \sin 60°$

$= 135 \text{ cm}^2$ (correct to 3 sig. fig.)

7. In the diagram, the vertices of the quadrilateral *ABCD* lie on a circle. *AB* = 4 cm, *BC* = 7 cm, *AC* = *CD* = 9 cm. Find
(a) ∠*ABC*,
(b) ∠*ACD*,
(c) the length of *AD*,
(d) the area of quadrilateral *ABCD*.

Solution

(a) In △*ABC*, by the cosine rule,

$\cos ∠ABC = \frac{4^2 + 7^2 - 9^2}{2 \times 4 \times 7}$

$= -0.2857$

$∠ABC = 106.60°$

$= 106.6°$ (correct to 1 d.p.)

(b) ∠*ADC* = 180° − ∠*ABC* (∠s in opp. segments)

= 180° − 106.6°

= 73.4°

∠*CAD* = ∠*ADC* (base ∠s of isos. △)

= 73.4°

∴ ∠*ACD* = 180° − 73.4° − 73.4° (∠ sum of △)

= 33.2°

(c) In △*ACD*, by the cosine rule,

$AD^2 = 9^2 + 9^2 - 2 \times 9 \times 9 \times \cos 33.2°$

$AD = \sqrt{26.444}$

$= 5.14$ cm (correct to 3 sig. fig.)

(d) Area of quadrilateral *ABCD*

= area of △*ABC* + area of △*ACD*

$= \frac{1}{2} \times 4 \times 7 \times \sin 106.6° + \frac{1}{2} \times 9 \times 9 \times \sin 33.2°$

$= 35.6 \text{ cm}^2$ (correct to 3 sig. fig.)

8.

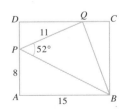

In the diagram, *ABCD* is a rectangle. *AB* = 15 cm, *AP* = 8 cm, *PQ* = 11 cm and ∠*BPQ* = 52°. Find
(a) the length of *BP*,
(b) the area of △*BPQ*,
(c) the length of *BQ*,
(d) the length of *BC*.

Solution

(a) $BP^2 = 8^2 + 15^2$ (Pythagoras' Theorem)

$BP = \sqrt{289}$

$= 17$ cm

(b) Area of △*BPQ*

$= \frac{1}{2} \times 11 \times 17 \times \sin 52°$

$= 73.679$

$= 73.7 \text{ cm}^2$ (correct to 3 sig. fig.)

(c) In △*BPQ*, by the cosine rule,

$BQ^2 = 11^2 + 17^2 - 2 \times 11 \times 17 \times \cos 52°$

$BQ = \sqrt{179.74}$

$= 13.407$

$= 13.4$ cm (correct to 3 sig. fig.)

(d) In △*ABP*,

$\tan ∠APB = \frac{15}{8}$

$∠APB = 61.93°$

$∠DPQ = 180° − 61.93° − 52°$

(adj. ∠s on a st. line)

$= 66.07°$

In △*DPQ*,

$\cos ∠DPQ = \frac{DP}{PQ}$

$DP = 11 \cos 66.07°$

$= 4.462$ cm

∴ $BC = AP + DP$

$= 8 + 4.462$

$= 12.462$

$= 12.5$ cm (correct to 3 sig. fig.)

9. In the diagram, a flagpole *BC* stands vertically on a terrace *CD*, and *AD* is horizontal ground. *AC* = 19 m, *AB* = 23 m and ∠*BAC* = 12°. Find
(a) the height of the flagpole *BC*,
(b) the height of the terrace *CD*,
(c) the area of △*ACD*.

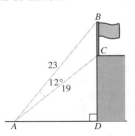

Solution

(a) In △*ABC*, by the cosine rule,

$BC^2 = 19^2 + 23^2 - 2 \times 19 \times 23 \times \cos 12°$

$BC = \sqrt{35.099}$

$= 5.9244$

$= 5.92$ m (correct to 3 sig. fig.)

∴ height of the flagpole is 5.92 m.

(b) By the sine rule,

$$\frac{19}{\sin \angle ABC} = \frac{5.9244}{\sin 12°}$$

$$\sin \angle ABC = \frac{19 \sin 12°}{5.9244}$$

$$\angle ABC = 41.82°$$

In $\triangle ABD$,

$$\cos \angle ABD = \frac{BD}{AB}$$

$$BD = 23 \cos 41.82°$$
$$= 17.1406 \text{ m}$$

∴ height of the terrace CD
$$= BD - BC$$
$$= 17.1406 - 5.9244$$
$$= 11.2162$$
$$= 11.2 \text{ m} \quad \text{(correct to 3 sig. fig.)}$$

(c) $\angle ACD = 12° + 41.82°$ (ext. ∠ of △)
$$= 53.82°$$

Area of $\triangle ACD = \frac{1}{2} \times 19 \times 11.2162 \times \sin 53.82°$
$$= 86.0 \text{ m}^2 \quad \text{(correct to 3 sig. fig.)}$$

10. The diagram shows a network of straight highways connecting four towns A, B, C and D. BCD is a straight highway. $AC = 25$ km, $CD = 22$ km, $DA = 41$ km and $\angle ABC = 76°$. Find

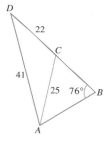

(a) $\angle ACD$,
(b) the shortest distance from C to AD,
(c) the distance BC,
(d) the area of $\triangle ABC$.

Solution

(a) In $\triangle ACD$, by the cosine rule,

$$\cos \angle ACD = \frac{22^2 + 25^2 - 41^2}{2 \times 22 \times 25}$$
$$= -0.52$$
$$\angle ACD = 121.33°$$
$$= 121.3° \quad \text{(correct to 1 d.p.)}$$

(b) Let h km be the perpendicular distance from C to AD.

Considering the area of $\triangle ACD$,

$$\frac{1}{2} \times h \times 41 = \frac{1}{2} \times 22 \times 25 \times \sin 121.33°$$
$$h = 11.46$$
$$= 11.5 \quad \text{(correct to 3 sig. fig.)}$$

∴ the shortest distance from C to AD is 11.5 km.

(c) $\angle BAC = 121.33° - 76°$ (ext. ∠ of △)
$$= 45.33°$$

In $\triangle ABC$, by the sine rule,

$$\frac{BC}{\sin 45.33°} = \frac{25}{\sin 76°}$$
$$BC = \frac{25 \sin 45.33°}{\sin 76°}$$
$$= 18.323$$
$$= 18.3 \text{ km} \quad \text{(correct to 3 sig. fig.)}$$

(d) $\angle BCA = 180° - 121.33°$ (adj. ∠s on a st. line)
$$= 58.67°$$

Area of $\triangle ABC$

$$= \frac{1}{2} \times 25 \times 18.323 \times \sin 58.67°$$
$$= 196 \text{ km}^2 \quad \text{(correct to 3 sig. fig.)}$$

Chapter 8   Applications Of Trigonometry

Extend Your Learning Curve

Drone of an Aeroplane

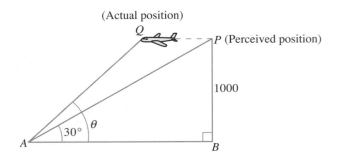

Kumar was reading a book at the location A on a level ground AB as shown in the diagram. Then he heard the drone of an aeroplane and it seemed that the aeroplane was at the position P with an angle of elevation of $30°$. When he looked at the sky, he noted that the aeroplane was actually at the position Q. Suppose the aeroplane was flying along the horizontal line PQ at a speed of 90 m/s and $PB = 1000$ m.

(a)   Explain why Kumar would have such a perception.

(b)   Find the angle of elevation of Q from A.

Take the speed of sound to be 340 m/s.

Solution

(a)   It takes time for the sound to travel from P to A. When the sound at P reaches A, the aeroplane has actually flown from P to Q. That is why Kumar would have such a perception.

(b)   In $\triangle ABP$,

$$\sin 30° = \frac{BP}{AP}$$

$$AP = \frac{1000}{\sin 30°}$$

$$= 2000 \text{ m}$$

Time taken for the sound to travel from P to $A = \dfrac{2000}{340}$

$$= \frac{100}{17} \text{ s}$$

$$\therefore \; PQ = 90 \times \frac{100}{17} = \frac{9000}{17} \text{ m}$$

Draw a perpendicular QN from Q to AB.

Then $AN = AB - PQ$

$$= 2000 \cos 30° - \frac{9000}{17}$$

In $\triangle ANQ$,

$$\tan \theta = \frac{NQ}{AN}$$

$$= \frac{9000}{17}$$

$$\theta = 39.7° \quad \text{(correct to 1 d.p.)}$$

$\therefore$ the angle of elevation of Q from A is $39.7°$.

Try It!

Section 8.1

1. A boat B is 4 km from a lighthouse L on a bearing of 320°.
   (a) Find the bearing of L from B.
   (b) A buoy Y is due North of L and due East of B. Find the distance LY.

Solution
(a)

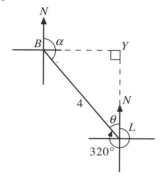

$$\theta = 360° - 320° \quad (\angle s \text{ at a point})$$
$$= 40°$$
$$\alpha = 180° - \theta \quad (\text{int. } \angle s, // \text{ lines})$$
$$= 180° - 40°$$
$$= 140°$$
$\therefore$ the bearing of L from B is 140°.

(b) In $\triangle BYL$,
$$\cos \theta = \frac{LY}{BL}$$
$$\therefore LY = 4 \cos 40°$$
$$= 3.06 \text{ km} \quad (\text{correct to 3 sig. fig.})$$

2. In the diagram, a house B is 400 m due South of a shop A. The bearings of a cafe C are 115° and 041° from A and B respectively. Find
   (a) the distance BC,
   (b) the shortest distance from C to the line AB.

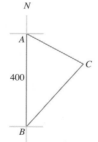

Solution
(a)

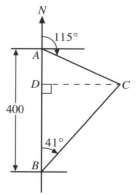

$$\angle BAC = 180° - 115° \quad (\text{adj. } \angle s \text{ on a st. line})$$
$$= 65°$$
$$\angle ACB = 115° - 41° \quad (\text{ext. } \angle \text{ of } \triangle)$$
$$= 74°$$
By the sine rule,
$$\frac{BC}{\sin 65°} = \frac{400}{\sin 74°}$$
$$BC = \frac{400 \sin 65°}{\sin 74°}$$
$$= 377.13$$
$$= 377 \text{ m} \quad (\text{correct to 3 sig. fig.})$$

(b) In $\triangle BCD$,
$$\sin 41° = \frac{CD}{BC}$$
$$\therefore CD = (377.13) \sin 41°$$
$$= 247 \text{ m} \quad (\text{correct to 3 sig. fig.})$$
i.e. the shortest distance from C to the line AB is 247 m.

3. The diagram shows the positions of a lighthouse H and two boats, A and B. The bearings of A and B from H are 131° and 054° respectively. $AH = 24$ km and $BH = 33$ km. Find
   (a) the distance between A and B,
   (b) the bearing of A from B.

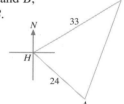

Solution
(a)

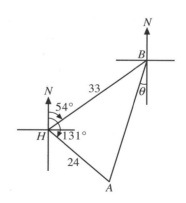

$$\angle AHB = 131° - 54°$$
$$= 77°$$
By the cosine rule,
$$AB^2 = 24^2 + 33^2 - 2 \times 24 \times 33 \times \cos 77°$$
$$AB = \sqrt{1308.68}$$
$$= 36.1756$$
$$= 36.2 \text{ km} \quad (\text{correct to 3 sig. fig.})$$

(b) By the sine rule,

$$\frac{24}{\sin \angle ABH} = \frac{36.1756}{\sin 77°}$$

$$\sin \angle ABH = \frac{24 \sin 77°}{36.1756}$$

$$\angle ABH = 40.3° \quad \text{(correct to 1 d.p.)}$$

$$40.3° + \theta = 54° \quad \text{(alt. } \angle s, \text{ // lines)}$$

$$\theta = 13.7°$$

Bearing of A from B

$$= 180° + 13.7°$$
$$= 193.7°$$
$$= 194° \quad \text{(correct to the nearest degree)}$$

Section 8.2

4. In the diagram, P is a point on the ground which is 5 m from a tree TQ. The angle of elevation of the top T of the tree from P is 41°. Find the height of the tree.

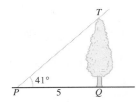

Solution

In $\triangle PQT$, $\qquad \tan 41° = \dfrac{TQ}{PQ}$

$$TQ = 5 \tan 41°$$
$$= 4.35 \text{ m}$$
$$\qquad \text{(correct to 3 sig. fig.)}$$

The height of the tree is 4.35 m.

5. In the diagram, TQ is a building of height 80 m. The angle of depression of a car P from the top T is 40°. Find the distance between P and Q.

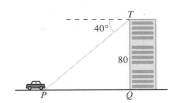

Solution

$$\angle QPT = 40° \qquad \text{(alt. } \angle s, \text{ // lines)}$$

$$\tan \angle QPT = \frac{TQ}{PQ}$$

$$\therefore \qquad PQ = \frac{80}{\tan 40°}$$

$$= 95.3 \text{ m} \quad \text{(correct to 3 sig. fig.)}$$

The distance between P and Q is 95.3 m.

6. In the diagram, MN is a vertical monument. A, N and B are at the same horizontal level. The angle of elevation of M from A is 40°. The angle of elevation of M from B is 54°. Given that $AB = 52$ m, find
(a) the length of BM,
(b) the height of the monument.

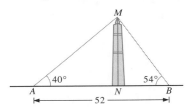

Solution

(a) $\angle AMB = 180° - 40° - 54° \quad (\angle \text{ sum of } \triangle)$

$$= 86°$$

In $\triangle ABM$, by the sine rule,

$$\frac{BM}{\sin 40°} = \frac{52}{\sin 86°}$$

$$BM = \frac{52 \sin 40°}{\sin 86°}$$

$$= 33.507$$

$$= 33.5 \text{ m} \quad \text{(correct to 3 sig. fig.)}$$

(b) In $\triangle BMN$,

$$\sin 54° = \frac{MN}{BM}$$

$$MN = (33.507)\sin 54°$$

$$= 27.1 \text{ m} \quad \text{(correct to 3 sig. fig.)}$$

The height of the monument is 27.1 m.

Section 8.3

7. In the diagram, $ABCDEFGH$ is a cuboid. $AB = 4$ cm, $BC = 3$ cm and $CG = 5$ cm. Find
(a) the length of the diagonal CE,
(b) $\angle ACE$.

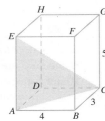

Solution

(a) In $\triangle ABC$,

$$AC^2 = 3^2 + 4^2 \qquad \text{(Pythagoras' Theorem)}$$
$$= 25$$

In $\triangle ACE$,

$$CE^2 = AE^2 + AC^2 \quad \text{(Pythagoras' Theorem)}$$
$$= 5^2 + 25$$
$$= 50$$

$$\therefore \quad CE = \sqrt{50}$$
$$= 7.07 \text{ cm} \qquad \text{(correct to 3 sig. fig.)}$$

(b) In $\triangle ACE$, $\qquad \sin \angle ACE = \dfrac{AE}{CE}$

$$= \frac{5}{\sqrt{50}}$$

$$\angle ACE = 45°$$

8. The diagram shows a right square pyramid. $AB = BC = 10$ cm, $VC = 15$ cm and M is the midpoint of BC. Find
   (a) the length of VM,
   (b) the height VN,
   (c) $\angle NMV$,
   (d) the volume of the pyramid.

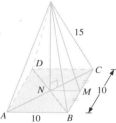

Solution

(a) In $\triangle CMV$,

$$CM = \frac{1}{2}BC$$
$$= 5 \text{ cm}$$
$$\angle VMC = 90°$$
$$VM^2 = 15^2 - 5^2 \quad \text{(Pythagoras' Theorem)}$$
$$VM = \sqrt{200}$$
$$= 14.1 \text{ cm} \quad \text{(correct to 3 sig. fig.)}$$

(b) In $\triangle MNV$,

$$MN = \frac{1}{2} \times 10$$
$$= 5 \text{ cm}$$
$$VN^2 = VM^2 - MN^2$$
$$= 200 - 5^2$$
$$VN = \sqrt{175}$$
$$= 13.2 \text{ cm} \quad \text{(correct to 3 sig. fig.)}$$

(c) In $\triangle MNV$,

$$\cos \angle NMV = \frac{MN}{VM}$$
$$= \frac{5}{\sqrt{200}}$$
$$\angle NMV = 69.3° \quad \text{(correct to 1 d.p.)}$$

(d) Volume of the pyramid
$$= \frac{1}{3} \times 10^2 \times \sqrt{175}$$
$$= 441 \text{ cm}^3 \quad \text{(correct to 3 sig. fig.)}$$

9. In the diagram, TC is a vertical building standing on a horizontal plane ABC. A is due South of C and B is due East of C. Suppose $BC = 30$ m and the angles of elevation of T from A and B are $30°$ and $45°$ respectively.
   (a) Find the height of the building.
   (b) Find the distance AC.
   (c) Find the bearing of B from A.

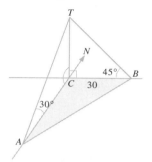

Solution

(a) In $\triangle BCT$,

$$\frac{TC}{BC} = \tan 45°$$
$$\frac{TC}{30} = \tan 45°$$
$$TC = 30 \tan 45°$$
$$= 30 \text{ m}$$

The height of the building is 30 m.

(b) In $\triangle ACT$,

$$\frac{TC}{AC} = \tan 30°$$
$$AC = \frac{TC}{\tan 30°}$$
$$= \frac{30}{\tan 30°}$$
$$= 51.96$$
$$= 52.0 \text{ m} \quad \text{(correct to 3 sig. fig.)}$$

(c) In $\triangle ABC$,

$$\tan \angle BAC = \frac{BC}{AC}$$
$$= \frac{30}{51.96}$$
$$\angle BAC = 30.0° \quad \text{(correct to 1 d.p.)}$$

$\therefore$ the bearing of B from A is $030.0°$.

Exercise 8.1
Basic Practice

1. Refer to the diagram. State the bearing of the point
   (a) A from O,
   (b) B from O,
   (c) C from O,
   (d) D from O.

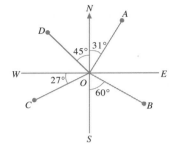

Solution

(a) The bearing of A from O is 031°.
(b) ∠NOB = 180° − 60°   (adj. ∠s on a st. line)
       = 120°
    The bearing of B from O is 120°.
(c) Reflex ∠NOC = 270° − 27°
            = 243°
    The bearing of C from O is 243°.
(d) Reflex ∠NOD = 360° − 45°   (∠s at a point)
            = 315°
    The bearing of D from O is 315°.

2. Refer to the diagram. State the bearing of
   (a) B from A,
   (b) C from A,
   (c) A from B,
   (d) A from C.

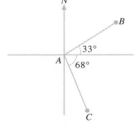

Solution

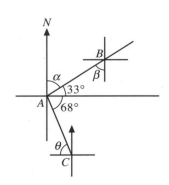

(a) $\alpha = 90° − 33°$
     $= 57°$
    The bearing of B from A is 057°.

(b) $90° + 68° = 158°$
    The bearing of C from A is 158°.
(c) $\beta = \alpha$ (alt. ∠s, // lines)
      $= 57°$
    $180° + \beta = 180° + 57°$
           $= 237°$
    The bearing of A from B is 237°.
(d) $\theta = 68°$ (alt. ∠s, // lines)
    $270° + 68° = 338°$
    The bearing of A from C is 338°.

3. The diagram shows the relative positions of three MRT stations. Find the bearing of
   (a) Woodlands from Orchard,
   (b) Orchard from Changi Airport,
   (c) Changi Airport from Woodlands.

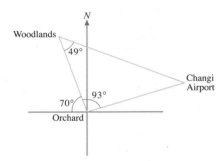

Solution

(a)

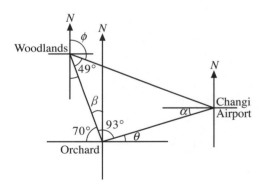

$270° + 70° = 340°$
The bearing of Woodlands from Orchard is 340°.

(b) $\theta = 180° − 70° − 93°$ (adj. ∠s on a st. line)
      $= 17°$
    $\alpha = \theta$ (alt. ∠s, // lines)
      $= 17°$
    $270° − \alpha = 270° − 17°$
            $= 253°$
    The bearing of Orchard from Changi Airport is 253°.

(c) $\beta = 90° - 70°$
$\qquad = 20°$
$\phi = 180° - 49° - 20°$ (adj. ∠s on a st. line)
$\qquad = 111°$
The bearing of Changi Airport from Woodlands is 111°.

4. Meili walks 4 km due West from her home H to a shop A and then walks 3 km due North to a cinema B. Find the distance and bearing of the cinema from her home.

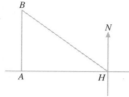

Solution
$\qquad BH^2 = AB^2 + AH^2$ (Pythagoras' Theorem)
$\qquad\quad = 3^2 + 4^2$
$\qquad BH = \sqrt{25}$
$\qquad\quad = 5$ km
The cinema is 5 km from her home.

$\qquad \tan \angle AHB = \dfrac{AB}{AH}$

$\qquad\qquad\quad = \dfrac{3}{4}$

$\qquad \angle AHB = 36.9°$ (correct to 1 d.p.)
$270° + \angle AHB = 270° + 36.9°$
$\qquad\qquad\qquad = 307°$ (correct to the nearest degree)
The bearing of the cinema from her home is 307°.

5. A ship A is 17 km on a bearing of 234° from a harbour H. Another ship B is 10 km on a bearing of 144° from H. Find
   (a) the distance between the ships A and B,
   (b) the bearing of B from A.

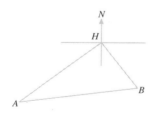

Solution
(a)

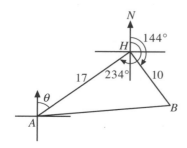

$\angle AHB = 234° - 144°$
$\qquad\quad = 90°$
$AB^2 = AH^2 + BH^2$ (Pythagoras' Theorem)
$\qquad = 17^2 + 10^2$
$AB = \sqrt{389}$
$\qquad = 19.7$ km   (correct to 3 sig. fig.)
The distance between the ships A and B is 19.7 km.

(b)
$\qquad\quad \theta = 234° - 180°$ (alt. ∠s, // lines)
$\qquad\qquad = 54°$

$\tan \angle BAH = \dfrac{10}{17}$

$\qquad \angle BAH = 30.47°$
$\theta + \angle BAH = 54° + 30.47°$
$\qquad\qquad = 84.47°$
$\qquad\qquad = 84°$ (correct to the nearest degree)
The bearing of B from A is 084°.

6. The diagram shows the relative positions of three cities A, B and C. The bearing of B from A is 063°. The bearing of C from B is 153°. $AB = 9$ km and $BC = 11$ km. Find
   (a) the distance AC,
   (b) the bearing of A from C.

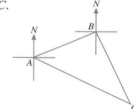

Solution
(a)

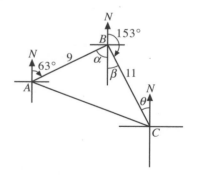

$\qquad \alpha = 63°$ (alt. ∠s, // lines)
$\qquad \beta = 180° - 153°$ (adj. ∠s on a st. line)
$\qquad\quad = 27°$
$\angle ABC = \alpha + \beta$
$\qquad\quad = 63° + 27°$
$\qquad\quad = 90°$
$AC^2 = 9^2 + 11^2$ (Pythagoras' Theorem)
$AC = \sqrt{202}$
$\qquad = 14.2$ km   (correct to 3 sig. fig.)

(b)
$$\theta = \beta \quad \text{(alt. } \angle\text{s, // lines)}$$
$$= 27°$$
$$\tan \angle ACB = \frac{9}{11}$$
$$\angle ACB = 39.29°$$
Bearing of A from C
$$= 360° - \theta - \angle ACB$$
$$= 360° - 27° - 39.29°$$
$$= 293.71°$$
$$= 294° \quad \text{(correct to the nearest degree)}$$

Further Practice

7. The diagram shows the relative positions of a hospital H and two buildings, A and B. A is due East of H, $AH = 7$ km, $AB = 5$ km and $\angle BAH = 69°$. Find the distance and bearing of B from H.

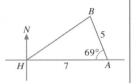

Solution
By the cosine rule,
$$BH^2 = 5^2 + 7^2 - 2 \times 5 \times 7 \times \cos 69°$$
$$BH = \sqrt{48.9142}$$
$$= 6.9939$$
$$= 6.99 \text{ km} \quad \text{(correct to 3 sig. fig.)}$$
$\therefore$ B is 6.99 km from H.
By the sine rule,
$$\frac{5}{\sin \angle AHB} = \frac{6.9939}{\sin 69°}$$
$$\sin \angle AHB = \frac{5 \sin 69°}{6.9939}$$
$$\angle AHB = 41.9° \quad \text{(correct to 1 d.p.)}$$
$$90° - \angle AHB = 90° - 41.9°$$
$$= 48.1°$$
$$= 48° \quad \text{(correct to the nearest degree)}$$
$\therefore$ the bearing of B from H is 048°.

8. In the diagram, C and D are two radar stations 4 km apart and C is due North of D. The bearings of a boat B are detected to be 110° and 038° from C and D respectively. Find
(a) the distance BC,
(b) the perpendicular distance from B to CD.

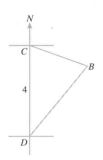

Solution

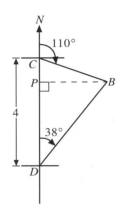

(a) $\angle CBD = 110° - 38° \quad$ (ext. $\angle$ of $\triangle$)
$$= 72°$$
By the sine rule,
$$\frac{BC}{\sin 38°} = \frac{4}{\sin 72°}$$
$$BC = \frac{4 \sin 38°}{\sin 72°}$$
$$= 2.5894$$
$$= 2.59 \text{ km} \quad \text{(correct to 3 sig. fig.)}$$

(b) In $\triangle BCP$,
$$\angle BCP = 180° - 110° \quad \text{(adj. } \angle\text{s on a st. line)}$$
$$= 70°$$
$$\sin \angle BCP = \frac{BP}{BC}$$
$$\therefore \quad BP = 2.5894 \sin 70°$$
$$= 2.43 \text{ km} \quad \text{(correct to 3 sig. fig.)}$$
i.e. the perpendicular distance from B to CD is 2.43 km.

9. In the diagram, A, B and C are the relative positions of three hotels. $AB = 6$ km, $BC = 5$ km and $CA = 4$ km. The bearing of B from A is 162°. Find
(a) $\angle BAC$,
(b) $\angle ACB$,
(c) the bearing of C from A,
(d) the bearing of B from C.

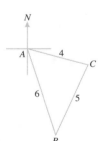

Solution
(a)

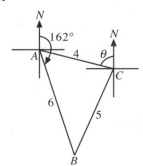

By the cosine rule,

$$\cos \angle BAC = \frac{6^2 + 4^2 - 5^2}{2 \times 6 \times 4}$$
$$= 0.5625$$
$$\angle BAC = 55.77°$$
$$= 55.8° \quad \text{(correct to 1 d.p.)}$$

(b) By the cosine rule,

$$\cos \angle ACB = \frac{4^2 + 5^2 - 6^2}{2 \times 4 \times 5}$$
$$= 0.125$$
$$\angle ACB = 82.82°$$
$$= 82.8° \quad \text{(correct to 1 d.p.)}$$

(c) $162° - \angle BAC$
$$= 162° - 55.8°$$
$$= 106.2°$$
$$= 106° \quad \text{(correct to the nearest degree)}$$
∴ the bearing of C from A is $106°$.

(d) $\theta = 180° - 106.2° \quad$ (int. ∠s, // lines)
$$= 73.8°$$
The bearing of B from C
$$= 360° - \angle ACB - \theta$$
$$= 360° - 82.8° - 73.8°$$
$$= 203.4°$$
$$= 203° \quad \text{(correct to the nearest degree)}$$

10. A point B is 500 m due North of a point A. Rahmat walks from A on a bearing of $325°$.

(a) Draw on the diagram the direction of Rahmat's path.

(b) Find Rahmat's distance from A when he is
   (i) due West of B,
   (ii) equidistant from A and B,
   (iii) closest to B.

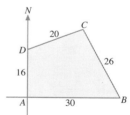

Solution

(a)

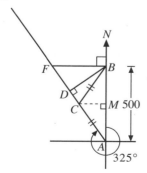

In the diagram, the ray $ACDF$ shows the direction of Rahmat's path.

(b) (i) F is the position when Rahmat is due West of B.
$$\angle BAF = 360° - 325° \quad \text{(∠s at a point)}$$
$$= 35°$$

In $\triangle BAF$,
$$\cos 35° = \frac{AB}{AF}$$
$$AF = \frac{500}{\cos 35°}$$
$$= 610 \text{ m} \quad \text{(correct to 3 sig. fig.)}$$
∴ the required distance is 610 m.

(ii) C is the position when Rahmat is equidistant from A and B.
In $\triangle ACM$,
$$AM = \frac{1}{2} AB$$
$$= \frac{1}{2} \times 500$$
$$= 250 \text{ m}$$
$$\cos 35° = \frac{AM}{AC}$$
$$\therefore \ AC = \frac{250}{\cos 35°}$$
$$= 305 \text{ m} \quad \text{(correct to 3 sig. fig.)}$$
∴ the required distance is 305 m.

(iii) D is the position when Rahmat is closest to B.
In $\triangle ABD$,
$$\cos 35° = \frac{AD}{AB}$$
$$AD = 500 \cos 35°$$
$$= 410 \text{ m} \quad \text{(correct to 3 sig. fig.)}$$
∴ the required distance is 410 m.

Maths@Work

11. In the diagram, $ABCD$ is a piece of land. B is due East of A and D is due North of A. $AB = 30$ m, $BC = 26$ m, $CD = 20$ m and $DA = 16$ m. Find

(a) the length of BD,
(b) $\angle ABC$,
(c) the bearing of C from B,
(d) the area of $ABCD$.

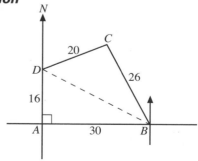

Solution

(a) In $\triangle ABD$,
$BD^2 = 16^2 + 30^2$ (Pythagoras' Theorem)
$BD = \sqrt{1156}$
    $= 34$ m

(b) In $\triangle ABD$,

$\tan \angle ABD = \dfrac{16}{30}$

  $\angle ABD = 28.07°$
In $\triangle BCD$,

$\cos \angle CBD = \dfrac{34^2 + 26^2 - 20^2}{2 \times 34 \times 26}$

        $= 0.809\ 95$
  $\angle CBD = 35.91°$
$\therefore$ $\angle ABC = \angle ABD + \angle CBD$
          $= 28.07° + 35.91°$
          $= 63.98°$
          $= 64.0°$ (correct to 1 d.p.)

(c) Bearing of C from B
  $= 270° + 64.0°$
  $= 334.0°$
  $= 334°$ (correct to the nearest degree)

(d) Area of $ABCD$
  $=$ area of $\triangle ABD +$ area of $\triangle BCD$

  $= \dfrac{1}{2} \times 16 \times 30 + \dfrac{1}{2} \times 26 \times 34 \times \sin 35.91°$

  $= 499$ m^2 (correct to 3 sig. fig.)

12. Two ships, A and B, leave a port P at the same time. A is on the course of 320° at 10 km/h. B is on the course of 240° at 15 km/h. After 2 hours,
(a) find the distance between A and B,
(b) find the bearing of B from A.

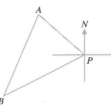

Solution
(a)

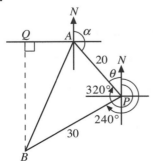

In the diagram,
$AP = 10 \times 2$
   $= 20$ km
$BP = 15 \times 2$
   $= 30$ km

$\angle APB = 320° - 240°$
       $= 80°$
By the cosine rule,
  $AB^2 = 20^2 + 30^2 - 2 \times 20 \times 30 \times \cos 80°$
   $AB = \sqrt{1091.62}$
      $= 33.040$
      $= 33.0$ km   (correct to 3 sig. fig.)

(b) By the sine rule,

   $\dfrac{30}{\sin \angle BAP} = \dfrac{33.04}{\sin 80°}$

  $\sin \angle BAP = \dfrac{30 \sin 80°}{33.04}$

    $\angle BAP = 63.4°$ (correct to 1 d.p.)
       $\theta = 360° - 320°$ ($\angle$s at a point)
       $\alpha = 180° - \theta$ (int. $\angle$s, // lines)
         $= 180° - 40°$
         $= 140°$
$\alpha + \angle BAP = 140° + 63.4°$
           $= 203.4°$
           $= 203°$ (correct to the nearest degree)
$\therefore$ the bearing of B from A is 203°.

13. The diagram shows 4 buildings A, B, C and D. C is due West of A and D is southeast of C. The bearing of B from A is 337° and the bearing of C from B is 232°. $AB = 8$ km and $CD = 7$ km. Find
(a) the distance between A and C,
(b) the distance between A and D,
(c) the bearing of D from A.

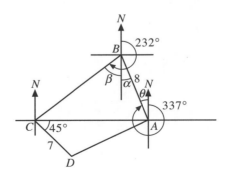

Solution
(a)

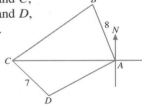

    $\theta = 360° - 337°$ ($\angle$s at a point)
      $= 23°$
$\angle CAB = 337° - 270°$
      $= 67°$
    $\alpha = \theta$ (alt. $\angle$s, // lines)
      $= 23°$

$$\beta = 232° - 180°$$
$$= 52°$$
$$\therefore \ \angle ABC = \alpha + \beta$$
$$= 23° + 52°$$
$$= 75°$$
$$\angle ACB = 180° - 67° - 75° \quad (\angle \text{ sum of } \triangle)$$
$$= 38°$$

In $\triangle ABC$, by the sine rule,
$$\frac{AC}{\sin 75°} = \frac{8}{\sin 38°}$$
$$AC = \frac{8 \sin 75°}{\sin 38°}$$
$$= 12.551$$
$$= 12.6 \text{ km}$$
i.e. the distance between A and C is 12.6 km.

(b) In $\triangle ACD$, by the cosine rule,
$$AD^2 = 7^2 + 12.551^2 - 2 \times 7 \times 12.551 \times \cos 45°$$
$$AD = \sqrt{82.2790}$$
$$= 9.0708$$
$$= 9.07 \text{ km} \quad (\text{correct to 3 sig. fig.})$$
i.e. the distance between A and D is 9.07 km.

(c) In $\triangle ACD$, by the sine rule,
$$\frac{7}{\sin \angle CAD} = \frac{9.0708}{\sin 45°}$$
$$\sin \angle CAD = \frac{7 \sin 45°}{9.0708}$$
$$\angle CAD = 33.07°$$
$$= 33° \quad (\text{correct to the nearest degree})$$
The bearing of D from $A = 270° - 33°$
$$= 237°$$

14. In the diagram, A, B and C are three shops along a straight road. B is 5 km on a bearing of 035° from A. A house D is 4 km on a bearing of 070° from A and $\angle BCD = 24°$. Find
(a) the distance BD,
(b) the distance BC.

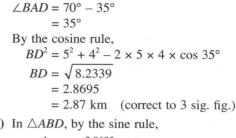

Solution
(a)

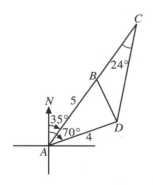

In $\triangle ABD$,
$$\angle BAD = 70° - 35°$$
$$= 35°$$
By the cosine rule,
$$BD^2 = 5^2 + 4^2 - 2 \times 5 \times 4 \times \cos 35°$$
$$BD = \sqrt{8.2339}$$
$$= 2.8695$$
$$= 2.87 \text{ km} \quad (\text{correct to 3 sig. fig.})$$

(b) In $\triangle ABD$, by the sine rule,
$$\frac{4}{\sin \angle ABD} = \frac{2.8695}{\sin 35°}$$
$$\sin \angle ABD = \frac{4 \sin 35°}{2.8695}$$
$$\angle ABD = 53.09°$$
In $\triangle BCD$,
$$\angle BDC = 53.09° - 24° \quad (\text{ext. } \angle \text{ of } \triangle)$$
$$= 29.09°$$
By the sine rule,
$$\frac{BC}{\sin 29.09°} = \frac{2.8695}{\sin 24°}$$
$$BC = \frac{(2.8695) \sin 29.09°}{\sin 24°}$$
$$= 3.43 \text{ km} \quad (\text{correct to 3 sig. fig.})$$

15. A school Q is 4 km northwest from a playground P. The bearing of a swimming pool R from P is 340°. R is 1.8 km from Q. Find
(a) the distance of R from P,
(b) the bearing of R from Q.

Solution
(a)

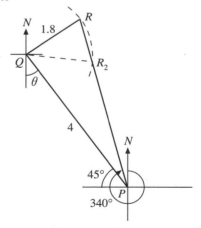

$$\angle QPR = (340° - 270°) - 45°$$
$$= 25°$$
By the sine rule,
$$\frac{4}{\sin \angle PRQ} = \frac{1.8}{\sin 25°}$$
$$\sin \angle PRQ = \frac{4 \sin 25°}{1.8}$$
$$\angle PRQ = 69.91° \text{ or } 180° - 69.91°$$
$$= 69.91° \text{ or } 110.09°$$

When∠PRQ = 69.91°,
∠PQR = 180° − 69.91° − 25°
= 85.09°
By the sine rule,
$$\frac{PR}{\sin 85.09°} = \frac{1.8}{\sin 25°}$$
$$PR = \frac{(1.8)\sin 85.09°}{\sin 25°}$$
= 4.24 km   (correct to 3 sig. fig.)
When∠PRQ = 110.09°
∠PQR = 180° − 110.09° − 25°
= 44.91°
By the sine rule,
$$\frac{PR}{\sin 44.91°} = \frac{1.8}{\sin 25°}$$
$$PR = \frac{(1.8)\sin 44.91°}{\sin 25°}$$
= 3.01 km   (correct to 3 sig. fig.)
Hence, the distance of R from P is 4.24 km or 3.01 km.

(b)   θ = 45°   (alt. ∠s, // lines)
Bearing of R from Q
= 180° − θ − ∠PQR
= 180° − 45° − 85.09° or 180° − 45° − 44.91°
= 49.91° or 90.09°
= 050° or 090°   (correct to the nearest degree)
Note: In the diagram, R and R₂ are the two possible positions of R.

Brainworks

16. The distance between two rescue centres, A and C, is 800 m. The bearings of a sinking boat B from A and C are 030° and 335° respectively. The distance AB is unknown. What further information is required to determine the distance AB? Illustrate your answer with a worked solution to the problem.

Solution

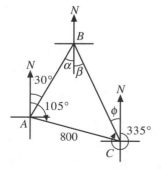

Any one of the following pieces of information can determine the distance AB:
1. the bearing of C from A;
2. ∠BAC;
3. ∠ACB;
4. the distance BC.

For instance, suppose the bearing of C from A is 105°. As shown in the figure,
α = 30°   (alt. ∠s, // lines)
β = φ   (alt. ∠s, // lines)
= 360° − 335°   (∠s at a point)
= 25°
∴ ∠ABC = α + β
= 55°
∠BAC = 105° − 30°
= 75°
∠ACB = 180° − 55° − 75°   (∠sum of △)
= 50°
By the sine rule,
$$\frac{AB}{\sin 50°} = \frac{800}{\sin 55°}$$
$$AB = \frac{800\sin 50°}{\sin 55°}$$
= 748 m   (correct to 3 sig. fig.)
∴ the distance AB is 748 m.

Exercise 8.2
Basic Practice

1. In the diagram, AC = 600 m. The angle of elevation of an aeroplane B from A is 52°. Find the height of the aeroplane above the ground.

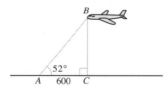

Solution
$$\tan 52° = \frac{BC}{AC}$$
$$BC = 600 \tan 52°$$
= 768 m   (correct to 3 sig. fig.)
The height of the aeroplane above the ground is 768 m.

2. In the diagram, the angle of elevation of the top F of a flagpole FM from a point A on the ground is 43°. Given that AM = 5 m, find
(a) the height of the flagpole,
(b) the distance AF.

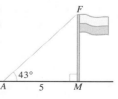

Solution
(a) $\tan 43° = \frac{FM}{AM}$
$FM = 5 \tan 43°$
= 4.66 m   (correct to 3 sig. fig.)
The height of the flagpole is 4.66 m.

(b) $\cos 43° = \dfrac{AM}{AF}$

$$AF = \dfrac{5}{\cos 43°}$$
$$= 6.84 \text{ m} \quad \text{(correct to 3 sig. fig.)}$$
∴ the distance AF is 6.84 m.

3. In the diagram, TF is a building of height 40 m. From the top T of the building, the angle of depression of a man M on the ground is 35°. Find the distance FM.

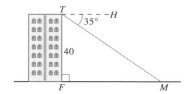

Solution

$∠FMT = 35°$ (alt. ∠s, $TH \parallel FM$)

$\tan ∠FMT = \dfrac{TF}{FM}$

$$FM = \dfrac{40}{\tan 35°}$$
$$= 57.1 \text{ m} \quad \text{(correct to 3 sig. fig.)}$$

4. In the diagram, B is a hot-air balloon above the ground level AC and $AB = 400$ m. The angle of depression of A from B is 29°. Find
    (a) the horizontal distance AC,
    (b) the height of the hot-air balloon above the ground.

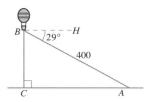

Solution

(a) $∠BAC = 29°$ (alt. ∠s, $BH \parallel CA$)

$\cos ∠BAC = \dfrac{AC}{AB}$

$$AC = 400 \cos 29°$$
$$= 350 \text{ m} \quad \text{(correct to 3 sig. fig.)}$$

(b) $\sin ∠BAC = \dfrac{BC}{AB}$

$$BC = 400 \sin 29°$$
$$= 194 \text{ m} \quad \text{(correct to 3 sig. fig.)}$$
The height of the hot-air balloon above the ground is 194 m.

5. In the diagram, A and B are two different levels in a building ABC. A point D is 50 m from the foot C of the building. The angles of elevation of A and B from D are 43° and 27° respectively. Find
    (a) the distance AD,
    (b) the distance AB.

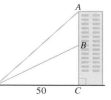

Solution

(a)   In $\triangle ACD$,

$$\cos 43° = \dfrac{CD}{AD}$$

$$AD = \dfrac{50}{\cos 43°}$$
$$= 68.4 \text{ m} \quad \text{(correct to 3 sig. fig.)}$$

(b)   In $\triangle ACD$,

$$\tan 43° = \dfrac{AC}{CD}$$
$$AC = 50 \tan 43°$$
$$= 46.625 \text{ m}$$
In $\triangle BCD$,
$$\tan 27° = \dfrac{BC}{CD}$$
$$BC = 50 \tan 27°$$
$$= 25.476 \text{ m}$$
∴ $AB = 46.625 - 25.476$
$$= 21.149$$
$$= 21.1 \text{ m} \quad \text{(correct to 3 sig. fig.)}$$

6. In the diagram, AB is a tower directly opposite a building CD and CD is 30 m high. The angle of elevation of A from C is 33°. The angle of depression of B from C is 29°. Find
    (a) the horizontal distance between the tower and the building,
    (b) the height of the tower.

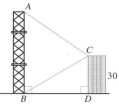

Solution

(a)

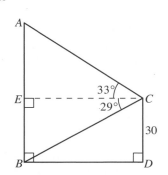

In $\triangle BCD$,

$\angle CBD = 29°$ (alt. $\angle$s, $EC // BD$)

$\tan \angle CBD = \dfrac{CD}{BD}$

$BD = \dfrac{30}{\tan 29°}$

    $= 54.121$

    $= 54.1$ m   (correct to 3 sig. fig.)

The horizontal distance between the tower and the building is 54.1 m.

(b) In $\triangle ACE$,

$\tan 33° = \dfrac{AE}{CE}$

    $AE = (54.121) \tan 33°$

        $= 35.147$ m

Height of the building

$= AE + EB$

$= 35.147 + 30$

$= 65.147$

$= 65.1$ m   (correct to 3 sig. fig.)

7. In the diagram, TF is a vertical building. A and B are two cars, 36 m apart, at the same level as the foot F of the building. The angles of depression of A and B from T are 29° and 51° respectively. Find

(a) the distance between A and T,

(b) the height of the building.

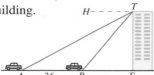

Solution

(a) In $\angle ABT$,

$\angle ABT = 180° - 51°$ (int. $\angle$s, $AB // HT$)

       $= 129°$

$\angle ATB = 51° - 29°$

       $= 22°$

By the sine rule,

$\dfrac{AT}{\sin 129°} = \dfrac{36}{\sin 22°}$

    $AT = \dfrac{36 \sin 129°}{\sin 22°}$

        $= 74.684$

        $= 74.7$ m   (correct to 3 sig. fig.)

The distance between A and T is 74.7 m.

(b) In $\triangle ATF$,

$\angle TAF = 29°$ (alt. $\angle$s, $HT // AB$)

$\sin \angle TAF = \dfrac{TF}{AT}$

    $TF = (74.684) \sin 29°$

        $= 36.2$ m   (correct to 3 sig. fig.)

The height of the building is 36.2 m.

8. In the diagram, AB is an advertisement board perched on a vertical pole BC. C and D are at the same horizontal level. $AB = 3$ m, $AD = 12$ m and $BD = 10$ m. Find

(a) the angle of elevation of A from D,

(b) the angle of elevation of B from D,

(c) the length of BC.

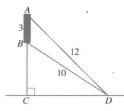

Solution

(a) In $\triangle ABD$, by the cosine rule,

$\cos \angle BAD = \dfrac{3^2 + 12^2 - 10^2}{2 \times 3 \times 12}$

             $= 0.7361$

    $\angle BAD = 42.60°$

In $\triangle ACD$,

$\angle CDA = 180° - 90° - 42.60°$

         $= 47.40°$

         $= 47.4°$ (correct to 1 d.p.)

$\therefore$ the angle of elevation of A from D is 47.4°.

(b) In $\triangle ABD$, by the cosine rule,

$\cos \angle ABD = \dfrac{3^2 + 10^2 - 12^2}{2 \times 3 \times 10}$

             $= -0.5833$

    $\angle ABD = 125.69°$

In $\triangle BCD$,

$90° + \angle BDC = 125.69°$ (ext. $\angle$ of $\triangle$)

    $\angle BDC = 35.69°$

         $= 35.7°$ (correct to 1 d.p.)

$\therefore$ the angle of elevation of B from D is 35.7°.

(c) In $\triangle BCD$,

$\sin \angle BDC = \dfrac{BC}{BD}$

    $BC = 10 \sin 35.69°$

       $= 5.83$ m   (correct to 3 sig. fig.)

Maths@Work

9. In the diagram, Ali stands 2.5 m in front of a tree. The angle of elevation of the top of the tree from his eyes is 40°. Ali's eye-level is 1.6 m from the ground. Find the height of the tree.

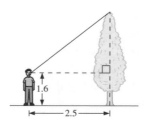

Solution

Let h m be the height of the tree.

$$\tan 40° = \frac{h - 1.6}{2.5}$$
$$h - 1.6 = 2.5 \tan 40°$$
$$h = 1.6 + (2.5) \tan 40°$$
$$= 3.70 \quad \text{(correct to 3 sig. fig.)}$$

The height of the tree is 3.70 m.

10. The diagram shows two different positions, P and Q, of a helicopter flying horizontally at a uniform speed of 72 km/h. It is found that it takes the helicopter 10 minutes to fly from P to Q. The angles of elevation of P and Q from a point A on the ground are 35° and 60° respectively. Find
   (a) the distance PQ,
   (b) the distance AP,
   (c) the height of the helicopter above the ground,
   (d) the time taken in minutes by the helicopter to fly horizontally from Q to the position directly above A.

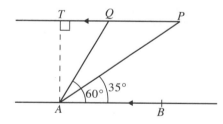

Solution
(a)

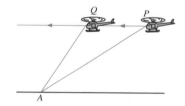

$$\text{Distance } PQ = 72 \times \frac{10}{60}$$
$$= 12 \text{ km}$$

(b) In $\triangle APQ$,
$$\angle AQP = 180° - 60° \quad (AB \, // \, QP)$$
$$= 120°$$
$$\angle PAQ = 60° - 35°$$
$$= 25°$$

By the sine rule,
$$\frac{AP}{\sin 120°} = \frac{12}{\sin 25°}$$
$$AP = \frac{12 \sin 120°}{\sin 25°}$$
$$= 24.59 \text{ km}$$
$$= 24.6 \text{ km} \quad \text{(correct to 3 sig. fig.)}$$

(c) In $\triangle APT$,
$$\angle APT = 35° \quad \text{(alt. } \angle\text{s, } AB \, // \, QP)$$
$$\sin \angle APT = \frac{AT}{AP}$$
$$AT = (24.59) \sin 35°$$
$$= 14.104$$
$$= 14.1 \text{ km} \quad \text{(correct to 3 sig. fig.)}$$

The height of the helicopter above the ground is 14.1 km.

(d) In $\triangle AQT$,
$$\angle AQT = 60° \quad \text{(alt. } \angle\text{s, } AB \, // \, QP)$$
$$\tan \angle AQT = \frac{AT}{QT}$$
$$QT = \frac{14.104}{\tan 60°}$$
$$= 8.1429 \text{ km}$$

The required time taken
$$= \frac{8.1429}{72} \times 60 \text{ min}$$
$$= 6.79 \text{ min} \quad \text{(correct to 3 sig. fig.)}$$

11. A and B are two houses, 40 m apart, on the same horizontal line as the foot F of a building TF. The angles of depression of A and B from the top T of the building are 25° and 58° respectively. Find the possible heights of the building.

Solution
Case 1
The two houses, A and B, are on the same side of the building.

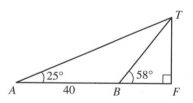

In $\triangle ABT$,
$$\angle ATB = 58° - 25° \quad \text{(ext. } \angle \text{ of } \triangle)$$
$$= 33°$$

By the sine rule,
$$\frac{BT}{\sin 25°} = \frac{40}{\sin 33°}$$
$$BT = \frac{40 \sin 25°}{\sin 33°}$$
$$= 31.038 \text{ m}$$

In $\triangle BFT$,
$$\sin 58° = \frac{TF}{BT}$$
$$TF = (31.038) \sin 58°$$
$$= 26.3 \text{ m} \quad \text{(correct to 3 sig. fig.)}$$

Case 2

The two houses, A and B, are on opposite sides of the building.

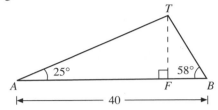

In $\triangle ABT$,

$\angle ATB = 180° - 25° - 58°$ ($\angle$ sum of $\triangle$)
$\quad\quad\quad = 97°$

By the cosine rule,

$$\frac{BT}{\sin 25°} = \frac{40}{\sin 97°}$$

$$BT = \frac{40 \sin 25°}{\sin 97°}$$
$$\quad\quad = 17.032 \text{ m}$$

In $\triangle BFT$,

$$\sin 58° = \frac{TF}{BT}$$

$$FT = (17.032) \sin 58°$$
$$\quad\quad = 14.4 \text{ m} \quad\quad\quad \text{(correct to 3 sig. fig.)}$$

$\therefore$ the possible heights of the building are 26.3 m and 14.4 m.

12. A flood light is hung in the middle of the high ceiling of a school hall. Assume that it is not easily accessible. Devise a method to find its perpendicular height from the ground.

Solution

First, we choose two points, A and B, on the floor of the hall such that A, B and the flood light L are on the same vertical plane (refer to the diagram). We then measure the distance, d metres, of AB, and the angles of elevation, α and β, of L from A and B.

In $\triangle ABL$, by the sine rule,

$$\frac{AL}{\sin \beta} = \frac{AB}{\sin[180° - (\alpha + \beta)]}$$

$$AL = \frac{d \sin \beta}{\sin (\alpha + \beta)}$$

In $\triangle ALN$,

$$\frac{LN}{AL} = \sin \alpha$$

$$AL = \sin \alpha$$

$$\quad = \frac{d \sin \alpha \sin \beta}{\sin (\alpha + \beta)} \text{ m}$$

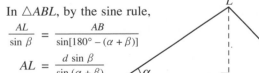

$\therefore$ the perpendicular height of the flood light is $\frac{d \sin \alpha \sin \beta}{\sin (\alpha + \beta)}$ metres.

Exercise 8.3
Basic Practice

1. In the diagram, $ABCDEFGH$ is a cube of side 5 cm. Find
   (a) the length of AC,
   (b) the length of AG,
   (c) $\angle GAC$.

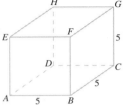

Solution

(a) In $\triangle ABC$,
$$AC^2 = 5^2 + 5^2 \quad \text{(Pythagoras' Theorem)}$$
$$AC = \sqrt{50}$$
$$\quad = 7.07 \text{ cm} \quad \text{(correct to 3 sig. fig.)}$$

(b) In $\triangle ACG$,
$$AG^2 = AC^2 + CG^2 \quad \text{(Pythagoras' Theorem)}$$
$$\quad\quad = 50 + 5^2$$
$$AG = \sqrt{75}$$
$$\quad = 8.66 \text{ cm} \quad \text{(correct to 3 sig. fig.)}$$

(c) In $\triangle ACG$,
$$\tan \angle GAC = \frac{GC}{AC}$$
$$\quad\quad\quad\quad = \frac{5}{\sqrt{50}}$$
$$\angle GAC = 35.3° \quad \text{(correct to 1 d.p.)}$$

2. In the diagram, $ABCDEFGH$ is a cuboid. $AB = 6$ cm, $BC = 8$ cm and $CG = 3$ cm. Find
   (a) the length of AC,
   (b) the length of CE,
   (c) $\angle AEC$,
   (d) $\angle CEH$.

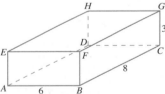

Solution

(a) In $\triangle ABC$,
$$AC^2 = 6^2 + 8^2 \quad \text{(Pythagoras' Theorem)}$$
$$AC = \sqrt{100}$$
$$\quad = 10 \text{ cm}$$

(b) In $\triangle ACE$,
$$CE^2 = AE^2 + AC^2 \quad \text{(Pythagoras' Theorem)}$$
$$\quad\quad = 3^2 + 100$$
$$CE = \sqrt{109}$$
$$\quad = 10.4 \text{ cm} \quad \text{(correct to 3 sig. fig.)}$$

(c) In $\triangle ACE$,

$$\tan \angle AEC = \frac{AC}{AE}$$

$$= \frac{10}{3}$$

$$\angle AEC = 73.3° \quad \text{(correct to 1 d.p.)}$$

(d) In $\triangle CEH$,

$$\cos \angle CEF = \frac{EH}{CE}$$

$$= \frac{8}{\sqrt{109}}$$

$$\angle CEF = 40.0° \quad \text{(correct to 1 d.p.)}$$

3.

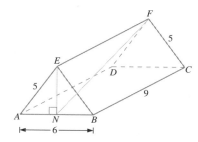

The diagram shows a triangular prism. $AE = BE = 5$ cm, $AB = 6$ cm, $BC = 9$ cm and $EN \perp AB$. Find

(a) the length of EN,

(b) the length of FN,

(c) $\angle ENF$.

Solution

(a) Since $AE = BE$,

$$AN = NB$$

$$= \frac{1}{2} AB$$

$$= 3 \text{ cm}$$

In $\triangle AEN$,

$$EN^2 = AE^2 - AN^2 \quad \text{(Pythagoras' Theorem)}$$

$$= 5^2 - 3^2$$

$$EN = \sqrt{16}$$

$$= 4 \text{ cm}$$

(b) In $\triangle EFN$,

$$FN^2 = EF^2 + EN^2 \quad \text{(Pythagoras' Theorem)}$$

$$= 9^2 + 4^2$$

$$FN = \sqrt{97}$$

$$= 9.85 \text{ cm} \quad \text{(correct to 3 sig. fig.)}$$

(c) In $\triangle EFN$,

$$\tan \angle ENF = \frac{EF}{EN}$$

$$= \frac{9}{4}$$

$$\angle ENF = 66.0° \quad \text{(correct to 1 d.p.)}$$

4. The diagram shows a right rectangular pyramid. $AB = 30$ cm, $BC = 16$ cm and $CV = 31$ cm. Find

(a) the length of AN,

(b) the height VN,

(c) $\angle VAN$,

(d) the volume of the pyramid.

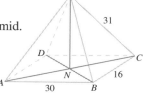

Solution

(a) In $\triangle ABC$,

$$AC^2 = 30^2 + 16^2 \quad \text{(Pythagoras' Theorem)}$$

$$AC = \sqrt{1156}$$

$$= 34 \text{ cm}$$

$$AN = \frac{1}{2} AC \quad \text{(diagonal of rectangle)}$$

$$= 17 \text{ cm}$$

(b) In $\triangle ANV$,

$$VN^2 = 31^2 - 17^2 \quad \text{(Pythagoras' Theorem)}$$

$$VN = \sqrt{672}$$

$$= 25.9 \text{ cm} \quad \text{(correct to 3 sig. fig.)}$$

(c) In $\triangle ANV$,

$$\cos \angle VAN = \frac{AN}{AV}$$

$$= \frac{17}{31}$$

$$\angle VAN = 56.7° \quad \text{(correct to 1 d.p.)}$$

(d) Volume of the pyramid

$$= \frac{1}{3} \times \text{area of } ABCD \times VN$$

$$= \frac{1}{3} \times 30 \times 16 \times \sqrt{672}$$

$$= 4150 \text{ cm}^2 \quad \text{(correct to 3 sig. fig.)}$$

Further Practice

5. In the diagram, $ABCDEFGH$ is a cuboid and M is the midpoint of AB. $AB = 6$ cm, $BC = 5$ cm and $CG = 4$ cm. Find

(a) the length of AC,

(b) the length of MG,

(c) $\angle CMG$,

(d) $\angle HMG$.

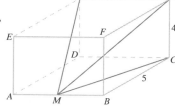

Solution

(a) In $\triangle ABC$,

$$AC^2 = 6^2 + 5^2 \quad \text{(Pythagoras' Theorem)}$$

$$AC = \sqrt{61}$$

$$= 7.81 \text{ cm} \quad \text{(correct to 3 sig. fig.)}$$

(b) $MB = \frac{1}{2}AB$

   $= 3$ cm

In $\triangle BCM$,

$CM^2 = 3^2 + 5^2$ (Pythagoras' Theorem)

   $= 34$

In $\triangle CGM$,

$MG^2 = CM^2 + CG^2$ (Pythagoras' Theorem)

   $= 34 + 4^2$

$MG = \sqrt{50}$

   $= 7.07$ cm   (correct to 3 sig. fig.)

(c) In $\triangle CGM$,

$\sin \angle CMG = \dfrac{CG}{MG}$

   $= \dfrac{4}{\sqrt{50}}$

$\angle CMG = 34.4°$ (correct to 1 d.p.)

(d) By symmetry,

   $MH = MG$

   $= \sqrt{50}$ cm

In $\triangle HMG$, by the cosine rule,

$\cos \angle HMG = \dfrac{(\sqrt{50})^2 + (\sqrt{50})^2 - 6^2}{2(\sqrt{50})(\sqrt{50})}$

   $= 0.64$

$\angle HMG = 50.2°$ (correct to 1 d.p.)

6. In the diagram, $\triangle ABC$ is an equilateral triangle of side 20 cm and it lies on a horizontal plane. VA is a vertical stick 21 cm long. M is the midpoint of BC. Find

(a) the length of MA,

(b) the length of VB,

(c) the length of VM,

(d) $\angle ABV$,

(e) $\angle AMV$.

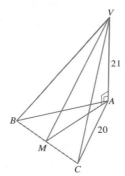

Solution

(a) $MC = \frac{1}{2}BC$

   $= 10$ cm

In $\triangle ACM$,

$MA^2 = 20^2 - 10^2$ (Pythagoras' Theorem)

$MA = \sqrt{300}$

   $= 17.3$ cm   (correct to 3 sig. fig.)

(b) In $\triangle ABV$,

$VB^2 = 20^2 + 21^2$ (Pythagoras' Theorem)

$VB = \sqrt{841}$

   $= 29$ cm

(c) By symmetry,

   $VB = VC$

Hence, $VM \perp BC$.

$VM^2 = 29^2 - 10^2$ (Pythagoras' Theorem)

$VM = \sqrt{741}$

   $= 27.2$ cm   (correct to 3 sig. fig.)

(d) In $\triangle ABV$,

$\tan \angle ABV = \dfrac{AV}{AB}$

   $= \dfrac{21}{20}$

$\angle ABV = 46.4°$ (correct to 1 d.p.)

(e) In $\triangle AMV$,

$\tan \angle AMV = \dfrac{AV}{MA}$

   $= \dfrac{21}{\sqrt{300}}$

$\angle AMV = 50.5°$ (correct to 1 d.p.)

7. The diagram shows a triangular prism in which $\angle BCE = 90°$, $BC = 18$ cm, $\angle CBE = 30°$ and $\angle AEB = 41°$. Find

(a) the length of CE,

(b) the length of BE,

(c) the length of AE,

(d) $\angle CAE$.

Solution

(a) In $\triangle BCE$,

$\tan 30° = \dfrac{CE}{BC}$

$CE = 18 \tan 30°$

   $= 10.3923$

   $= 10.4$ cm   (correct to 3 sig. fig.)

(b) In $\triangle BCE$,

$\cos 30° = \dfrac{BC}{BE}$

$BE = \dfrac{18}{\cos 30°}$

   $= 20.7846$

   $= 20.8$ cm   (correct to 3 sig. fig.)

(c) In $\triangle ABE$,

$\cos 41° = \dfrac{BE}{AE}$

$AE = \dfrac{20.7846}{\cos 41°}$

   $= 27.5399$

   $= 27.5$ cm   (correct to 3 sig. fig.)

(d) In $\triangle ACE$,

$\sin \angle CAE = \dfrac{CE}{AE}$

   $= \dfrac{10.3923}{27.5399}$

$\angle CAE = 22.2°$ (correct to 1 d.p.)

Maths@Work

8. In the diagram, *ABCD* is a door 1 m wide and 2 m long. It is hinged along *AB* and opens by 38° to the position *ABEF*. Find
(a) the distance *CE*,
(b) the length of *AE*,
(c) ∠*CAE*.

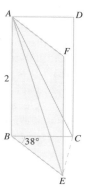

Solution

(a) In △*BCE*,
$$BC = BE$$
$$= 1 \text{ m}$$
By the cosine rule,
$$CE^2 = 1^2 + 1^2 - 2 \times 1 \times 1 \times \cos 38°$$
$$CE = \sqrt{0.423\,978}$$
$$= 0.6511$$
$$= 0.651 \text{ m} \quad \text{(correct to 3 sig. fig.)}$$

(b) In △*ABE*,
$$AE^2 = 2^2 + 1^2 \quad \text{(Pythagoras' Theorem)}$$
$$AE = \sqrt{5}$$
$$= 2.2361$$
$$= 2.24 \text{ m} \quad \text{(correct to 3 sig. fig.)}$$

(c) In △*ACE*, *AE* = *AC*, by the cosine rule,
$$\cos ∠CAE = \frac{(\sqrt{5})^2 + (\sqrt{5})^2 - 0.423\,978}{2 \times \sqrt{5} \times \sqrt{5}}$$
$$= 0.9576$$
$$∠CAE = 16.7° \quad \text{(correct to 1 d.p.)}$$

9. In the diagram, *TC* is a vertical building of height 75 m standing on horizontal ground *ABC*. *A* is due South of *C* and *B* is due East of *C*. The angles of elevation of *T* from *A* and *B* are 32° and 50° respectively. Find
(a) the distance *AC*,
(b) the distance *BC*,
(c) the distance *AB*,
(d) the bearing of *A* from *B*.

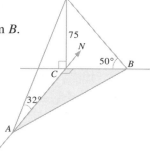

Solution

(a) In △*ACT*,
$$\tan 32° = \frac{TC}{AC}$$
$$AC = \frac{75}{\tan 32°}$$
$$= 120.03$$
$$= 120 \text{ m} \quad \text{(correct to 3 sig. fig.)}$$

(b) In △*BCT*,
$$\tan 50° = \frac{TC}{BC}$$
$$BC = \frac{75}{\tan 50°}$$
$$= 62.932$$
$$= 62.9 \text{ m} \quad \text{(correct to 3 sig. fig.)}$$

(c) In △*ABC*,
$$AB^2 = AC^2 + BC^2$$
$$= 120.03^2 + 62.932^2$$
$$AB = \sqrt{18\,367.6}$$
$$= 135.53$$
$$= 136 \text{ m} \quad \text{(correct to 3 sig. fig.)}$$

(d) In △*ABC*,
$$\tan ∠ABC = \frac{AC}{BC}$$
$$= \frac{120.03}{62.932}$$
$$∠ABC = 62.33°$$
$$= 62° \quad \text{(correct to the nearest degree)}$$
$$270° - 62° = 208°$$
∴ the bearing of *A* from *B* is 208°.

10. The diagram shows a North-facing hill slope. *AE* is a path on the slope and the bearing of *C* from *A* is 038°. *ABEF* and *ABCD* are rectangles. *BE* = 70 m and ∠*CBE* = 25°. Find
(a) the length of *CE*,
(b) the length of *BC*,
(c) the length of *AC*,
(d) ∠*CAE*.

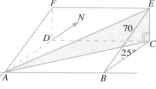

Solution

(a) In △*BCE*,
$$\sin 25° = \frac{CE}{BE}$$
$$CE = 70 \sin 25°$$
$$= 29.583$$
$$= 29.6 \text{ m} \quad \text{(correct to 3 sig. fig.)}$$

(b) In △*BCE*,
$$\cos 25° = \frac{BC}{BE}$$
$$BC = 70 \cos 25°$$
$$= 63.442$$
$$= 63.4 \text{ m} \quad \text{(correct to 3 sig. fig.)}$$

(c) ∠*CAD* = 38° (given)
∠*ACB* = ∠*CAD* (alt. ∠s, *AD* // *BC*)
$$= 38°$$
In △*ABC*,
$$\cos 38° = \frac{BC}{AC}$$
$$AC = \frac{63.442}{\cos 38°}$$
$$= 80.509$$
$$= 80.5 \text{ m} \quad \text{(correct to 3 sig. fig.)}$$

(d) In △ACE,

$$\tan \angle CAE = \frac{CE}{AC}$$

$$= \frac{29.583}{80.509}$$

$$\angle CAE = 20.2° \quad \text{(correct to 1 d.p.)}$$

11. In the diagram, ABC is a horizontal triangular field. $AB = 120$ m, $\angle CAB = 42°$ and $\angle ABC = 35°$. TC is a vertical building standing on ABC. The angle of elevation of T from A is $39°$. Find

(a) the length of AC,

(b) the length of BC,

(c) the height of the building,

(d) the angle of elevation of T from B.

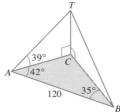

Solution

(a) In △ABC,

$$\angle ACB = 180° - 42° - 35° \quad (\angle \text{ sum of } \triangle)$$

$$= 103°$$

By the sine rule,

$$\frac{AC}{\sin 35°} = \frac{120}{\sin 103°}$$

$$AC = \frac{120 \sin 35°}{\sin 103°}$$

$$= 70.640$$

$$= 70.6 \text{ m} \quad \text{(correct to 3 sig. fig.)}$$

(b) In △ABC, by the sine rule,

$$\frac{BC}{\sin 42°} = \frac{120}{\sin 103°}$$

$$BC = \frac{120 \sin 42°}{\sin 103°}$$

$$= 82.408$$

$$= 82.4 \text{ m} \quad \text{(correct to 3 sig. fig.)}$$

(c) In △ACT,

$$\tan 39° = \frac{TC}{AC}$$

$$TC = (70.640) \tan 39°$$

$$= 57.203$$

$$= 57.2 \text{ m} \quad \text{(correct to 3 sig. fig.)}$$

∴ the height of the building is 57.2 m.

(d) In △BCT,

$$\tan \angle CBT = \frac{TC}{BC}$$

$$= \frac{57.203}{82.408}$$

$$\angle CBT = 34.8° \quad \text{(correct to 1 d.p.)}$$

i.e. the angle of elevation of T from B is 34.8°.

12. In the diagram, XY is a straight road on the same horizontal level as the foot C of a vertical building TC. A is a point on XY such that $AC = 60$ m, $\angle CAY = 35°$ and the angle of elevation of T from A is $28°$.

(a) Find the height of the building.

(b) B is another spot on XY such that the angle of elevation of T from B is $41°$. Find the possible distances of AB.

Solution

(a) In △ACT,

$$\tan 28° = \frac{TC}{AC}$$

$$TC = 60 \tan 28°$$

$$= 31.903$$

$$= 31.9 \text{ m} \quad \text{(correct to 3 sig. fig.)}$$

i.e. the height of the building is 31.9 m.

(b) In △BCT,

$$\tan 41° = \frac{TC}{BC}$$

$$BC = \frac{31.903}{\tan 41°}$$

$$= 36.700 \text{ m}$$

In △ABC, by the sine rule,

$$\frac{60}{\sin \angle ABC} = \frac{36.7}{\sin 35°}$$

$$\sin \angle ABC = \frac{60 \sin 35°}{36.7}$$

$$\angle ABC = 69.67° \text{ or } 180° - 69.67°$$

$$= 69.67° \text{ or } 110.33°$$

When $\angle ABC = 69.67°$,

$$\angle ACB = 180° - 35° - 69.67° \quad (\angle \text{ sum of } \triangle)$$

$$= 75.33°$$

By the sine rule,

$$\frac{AB}{\sin 75.33°} = \frac{60}{\sin 69.67°}$$

$$AB = \frac{60 \sin 75.33°}{\sin 69.67°}$$

$$= 61.9 \text{ m} \quad \text{(correct to 3 sig. fig.)}$$

When $\angle ABC = 110.33°$,

$$\angle ACB = 180° - 35° - 110.33° \quad (\angle \text{ sum of } \triangle)$$

$$= 34.67°$$

By the sine rule,

$$\frac{AB}{\sin 34.67°} = \frac{60}{\sin 110.33°}$$

$$AB = \frac{60 \sin 34.67°}{\sin 110.33°}$$

$$= 36.4 \text{ m} \quad \text{(correct to 3 sig. fig.)}$$

Hence, the possible distances of AB are 61.9 m and 36.4 m.

Brainworks

13. For sending an air parcel to an overseas destination, a post office has a restriction on the size of the air parcel. Suppose you are allowed to send a rectangular box whose length is 1.05 m and the sum of the width and the height is 1 m. Determine the minimum length of the diagonal of the box.

Solution

Let x m be the width of the box and y m by the length of the diagonal of the box.

Then $y^2 = 1.05^2 + x^2 + (1 - x)^2$ for $0 < x < 1$.

$$y^2 = 1.1025 + x^2 + 1 - 2x + x^2$$
$$= 2x^2 - 2x + 2.1025$$
$$= 2(x^2 - x) + 2.1025$$
$$= 2\left[x^2 - x + \left(-\frac{1}{2}\right)^2 - \left(-\frac{1}{2}\right)^2\right] + 2.1025$$
$$= 2\left(x - \frac{1}{2}\right)^2 + 1.6025$$
$$\therefore\ y = \sqrt{2\left(x - \frac{1}{2}\right)^2 + 1.6025}$$

When $x = \frac{1}{2}$, y is minimum.

Minimum value of $y = \sqrt{1.6025}$
   $= 1.27$ (correct to 3 sig. fig.)

∴ the minimum length of the diagonal is 1.27 m.

Note: Students may use a spreadsheet to explore the value of y for $x = 0, 0.1, 0.2, ..., 1$.

Revision Exercise 8

1. In the diagram, A, D and C are three spots on a horizontal straight road. B is a hot-air balloon hovering directly above D. $AD = 150$ m, $BC = 330$ m and $\angle ABD = 36°$. Find
   (a) the angle of depression of A from B,
   (b) the height of the hot-air balloon above the ground,
   (c) the angle of elevation of B from C,
   (d) the distance AC.

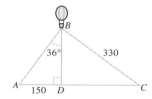

Solution

(a) Angle of depression of A from $B = 90° - 36°$
    $= 54°$

(b) In $\triangle ABD$,

   $\tan 36° = \dfrac{150}{BD}$

   $BD = \dfrac{150}{\tan 36°}$
   $= 206.46$
   $= 206$ m   (correct to 3 sig. fig.)

   The height of the hot-air balloon above the ground is 206 m.

(c) In $\triangle BCD$,

   $\sin \angle BCD = \dfrac{BD}{BC}$
   $= \dfrac{206.46}{330}$

   $\angle BCD = 38.73°$
   $= 38.7°$ (correct to 1 d.p.)

   The angle of elevation of B from C is 38.7°.

(d) In $\triangle BCD$,

   $\cos \angle BCD = \dfrac{CD}{BC}$

   $CD = 330 \cos 38.73°$
   $= 257.43$ m

   $AC = AD + CD$
   $= 150 + 257.43$
   $= 407.43$
   $= 407$ m   (correct to 3 sig. fig.)

2. In the diagram, P is a post office. A shop A is 480 m due West of P. Another shop B is 480 m on a bearing of 220° from P. Find
   (a) $\angle ABP$,
   (b) the bearing of A from B,
   (c) the bearing of P from B,
   (d) the distance AB.

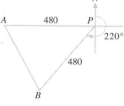

Solution

(a)

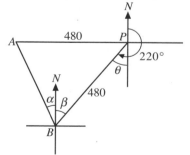

$\angle APB = 270° - 220°$
   $= 50°$

$\angle ABP = \angle BAP$ (base $\angle$s of isos. $\triangle$)

$\angle ABP + \angle BAP + 50° = 180°$ ($\angle$ sum of $\triangle$)

$\therefore\ 2\angle ABP = 130°$

$\angle ABP = 65°$

(b)
$$\theta = 220° - 180°$$
$$= 40°$$
$$\beta = \theta \quad \text{(alt. } \angle\text{s, //lines)}$$
$$= 40°$$
$$\alpha + \beta = 65°$$
$$\alpha + 40° = 65$$
$$\alpha = 25°$$
$$360° - \alpha = 360° - 25°$$
$$= 335°$$
∴ the bearing of A from B is 335°.

(c) The bearing of P from B is 040°.

(d) In $\triangle ABP$, by the cosine rule,
$$AB^2 = 480^2 + 480^2 - 2 \times 480 \times 480 \times \cos 50°$$
$$AB = \sqrt{164\ 603}$$
$$= 405.71$$
$$= 406 \text{ m} \quad \text{(correct to 3 sig. fig.)}$$

3. In the diagram, A and B are two towns. B is 26 km on a bearing of 120° from A. BP is a straight road and $\angle ABP = 40°$.

(a) Find the shortest distance from A to the road BP.

(b) C is another town on BP such that $AC = 19$ km. Find

  (i) the possible distances of BC,

  (ii) the possible bearings of C from A.

Solution

(a)

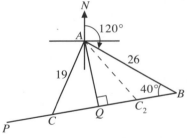

In the diagram, AQ is the shortest distance from A to the road BP.

In $\triangle ABQ$,
$$\sin 26° = \frac{AQ}{AB}$$
$$AQ = 26 \sin 40°$$
$$= 16.7 \text{ km} \quad \text{(correct to 3 sig. fig.)}$$
∴ the shortest distance from A to the road BP is 16.7 km.

(b) (i) In $\triangle ABC$, by the sine rule,
$$\frac{26}{\sin \angle ACB} = \frac{19}{\sin 40°}$$
$$\sin \angle ACB = \frac{26 \sin 40°}{19}$$

$$\angle ACB = 61.59° \text{ or } 180° - 61.59°$$
$$= 61.59° \text{ or } 118.41°$$
When $\angle ACB = 61.59°$,
$$\angle CAB = 180° - 61.59° - 40° \quad (\angle \text{ sum}$$
$$= 78.41° \qquad\qquad \text{of } \triangle)$$
By the sine rule,
$$\frac{BC}{\sin 78.41°} = \frac{19}{\sin 40°}$$
$$BC = \frac{19 \sin 78.41°}{\sin 40°}$$
$$= 29.0 \text{ km}$$
When $\angle ACB = 118.41°$,
$$\angle CAB = 180° - 118.41° - 40° \quad (\angle \text{ sum}$$
$$= 21.59° \qquad\qquad \text{of } \triangle)$$
By the sine rule,
$$\frac{BC}{\sin 21.59°} = \frac{19}{\sin 40°}$$
$$BC = \frac{19 \sin 21.59°}{\sin 40°}$$
$$= 10.9 \text{ km}$$
∴ the possible distances of BC are 29.0 km and 10.9 km.

Note: In the diagram, C_2 is the second possible position of C.

(ii) The possible bearings of A from C
$$= 120° + 78.41° \text{ or } 120° + 21.59°$$
$$= 198.41° \text{ or } 141.59°$$
$$= 198° \text{ or } 142° \quad \text{(correct to the nearest}$$
$$\text{degree)}$$

4. Ada and Ben left a hawker centre H at noon. Ada walked at 4 km/h on a bearing of 032°. Ben walked at 5 km/h on a bearing of 290°. At 2 p.m., Ada was at A and Ben was at B.

(a) Find the distance and bearing of B from A.

(b) If M is the midpoint of AB, find the distance and bearing of M from H.

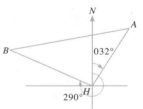

Solution

(a)

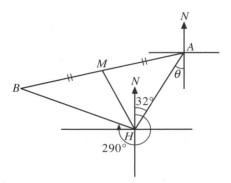

In △ABH,

$$\angle AHB = (360° - 290°) + 32°$$
$$= 102°$$
$$AH = 4 \times 2$$
$$= 8 \text{ km}$$
$$BH = 5 \times 2$$
$$= 10 \text{ km}$$

By the cosine rule,

$$AB^2 = 8^2 + 10^2 - 2 \times 8 \times 10 \times \cos 102°$$
$$AB = \sqrt{197.266}$$
$$= 14.045$$
$$= 14.0 \text{ km} \quad \text{(correct to 3 sig. fig.)}$$

By the sine rule,

$$\frac{10}{\sin \angle BAH} = \frac{14.045}{\sin 102°}$$
$$\sin \angle BAH = \frac{10 \sin 102°}{14.045}$$
$$\angle BAH = 44.14°$$
$$\theta = 32° \quad \text{(alt. } \angle s, \text{ // lines)}$$

Bearing of B from A

$$= 180° + \theta + \angle BAH$$
$$= 180° + 32° + 44.14°$$
$$= 256.14°$$
$$= 256° \quad \text{(correct to the nearest degree)}$$

(b)

$$AM = \frac{1}{2}AB$$
$$= \frac{1}{2} \times 14.045$$
$$= 7.0225 \text{ km}$$

In △AHM, by the sine rule,

$$HM^2 = 7.0225^2 + 8^2 - 2 \times 7.0225 \times 8$$
$$\times \cos 44.14°$$
$$HM = \sqrt{32.6814}$$
$$= 5.7168$$
$$= 5.72 \text{ km}$$

By the sine rule,

$$\frac{7.0225}{\sin \angle AHM} = \frac{5.7168}{\sin 44.14°}$$
$$\sin \angle AHM = \frac{(7.0225) \sin 44.14°}{5.7168}$$
$$\angle AHM = 58.8° \quad \text{(correct to 1 d.p.)}$$

Bearing of M from H

$$= 360° - (58.8° - 32°)$$
$$= 333.2°$$
$$= 333° \quad \text{(correct to the nearest degree)}$$

5.

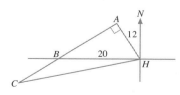

In the diagram, the line segments HA and ABC constitute the course of a ship which left a harbour H at noon to sail to A and then to C at a uniform speed. HA = 12 km and HB = 20 km. ∠HAB = 90° and B is due West of H.

(a) Find the distance AB.

(b) Find ∠ABH.

(c) Find the bearing of A from H.

(d) The ship reached B at 2 p.m.

   (i) Find the uniform speed of the ship.

   (ii) If the ship reached C at 3 p.m., find the distance and the bearing of C from H.

Solution

(a) In △ABH,

$$AB^2 = 20^2 - 12^2 \quad \text{(Pythagoras' Theorem)}$$
$$AB = \sqrt{256}$$
$$= 16 \text{ km}$$

(b) In △ABH,

$$\sin \angle ABH = \frac{12}{20}$$
$$\angle ABH = 36.87°$$
$$= 36.9° \quad \text{(correct to 1 d.p.)}$$

(c) $\angle AHB = 180° - 90° - 36.87°$
$$= 53.13°$$

Bearing of A from H

$$= 270° + 53.13°$$
$$= 323.13°$$
$$= 323° \quad \text{(correct to the nearest degree)}$$

(d) (i) Distance travelled from noon to 2 p.m.

$$= HA + AB$$
$$= 12 + 16$$
$$= 28 \text{ km}$$

Uniform speed of the ship

$$= 28 \div 2$$
$$= 14 \text{ km/h}$$

(ii)

$$BC = 14 \times 1$$
$$= 14 \text{ km}$$
$$AC = 14 + 16$$
$$= 30 \text{ km}$$
$$\angle BCH = 180° - 36.87° \text{ (adj. } \angle s \text{ on a st. line)}$$
$$= 143.13°$$

In △ACH,

$$CH^2 = 12^2 + 30^2 \quad \text{(Pythagoras' Theorem)}$$
$$CH = \sqrt{1044}$$
$$= 32.31$$
$$= 32.3 \text{ km} \quad \text{(correct to 3 sig. fig.)}$$
$$\tan \angle AHC = \frac{30}{12}$$
$$\angle AHC = 68.20°$$

∴ bearing of C from H

$$= 270° - (68.20° - 53.13°)$$
$$= 254.93°$$
$$= 255° \quad \text{(correct to the nearest degree)}$$

6. In the diagram, T is a spot on a flyover and XY is a horizontal road below it. The angles of depression of two cars A and B from T are 38° and 56° respectively. The length of AB is 45 m.

(a) Find the length of AT.

(b) Find the height of T above the road XY.

(c) If another car D on the road is 10 m from the car A, find the possible angles of elevation of T from D.

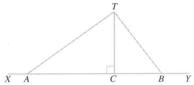

Solution

(a)

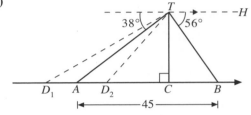

In $\triangle ABT$,

$\angle ATB = 180° - 38° - 56°$ ($\angle$ sum of $\triangle$)

     $= 86°$

$\angle ABT = 56°$ (alt. $\angle$s, AB // TH)

By the sine rule,

$$\frac{AT}{\sin 56°} = \frac{45}{\sin 86°}$$

$$AT = \frac{45 \sin 56°}{\sin 86°}$$

     $= 37.398$

     $= 37.4$ m   (correct to 3 sig. fig.)

(b) In $\triangle ACT$,

     $\angle CAT = 38°$ (alt. $\angle$s, AB // TH)

$$\sin \angle CAT = \frac{TC}{AT}$$

     $TC = (37.398) \sin 38°$

         $= 23.025$

         $= 23.0$ m

The height of T above the road is 23.0 m.

(c) In the diagram, D_1 and D_2 are two possible positions of D.

In $\triangle ACT$,

$$\cos 38° = \frac{AC}{AT}$$

     $AC = (37.398) \cos 38°$

         $= 29.470$

$\therefore$ $D_1C = 10 + 29.470$

         $= 39.470$ km

and $D_2C = 29.470 - 10$

            $= 19.470$ km

In $\triangle CD_1T$,

$$\tan \angle CD_1T = \frac{TC}{D_1C}$$

             $= \frac{23.025}{39.470}$

   $\angle CD_1T = 30.3°$ (correct to 1 d.p.)

In $\triangle CD_2T$,

$$\tan \angle CD_2T = \frac{TC}{D_2C}$$

             $= \frac{23.025}{19.470}$

   $\angle CD_2T = 49.8°$ (correct to 1 d.p.)

$\therefore$ the possible angles of elevation of T from D are 30.3° and 49.8°.

7. The diagram shows a right square pyramid. $AB = 10$ cm and $\angle VAN = 70°$. Find

(a) the length of AC,

(b) the length of AV,

(c) the length of VN,

(d) the length of VM, where M is the midpoint of BC,

(e) the volume of the pyramid,

(f) the total surface area of the pyramid,

(g) $\angle VMN$.

Solution

(a) In $\triangle ABC$,

$AC^2 = 10^2 + 10^2$ (Pythagoras' Theorem)

$AC = \sqrt{200}$

     $= 14.142$

     $= 14.1$ cm   (correct to 3 sig. fig.)

(b) $AN = \frac{1}{2}AC$ (diagonal of a square)

           $= \frac{1}{2} \times 14.142$

           $= 7.071$ cm

In $\triangle ANV$,

$$\cos 70° = \frac{AN}{AV}$$

     $AV = \frac{7.071}{\cos 70°}$

         $= 20.674$

         $= 20.7$ cm   (correct to 3 sig. fig.)

(c) In $\triangle ANV$,

$$\tan 70° = \frac{VN}{AN}$$

     $VN = (7.071) \tan 70°$

         $= 19.427$

         $= 19.4$ cm   (correct to 3 sig. fig.)

(d) In $\triangle MNV$,

$$MN = \frac{1}{2}AB$$
$$= 5 \text{ cm}$$
$$VM^2 = VN^2 + MN^2 \quad \text{(Pythagoras' Theorem)}$$
$$= 19.427^2 + 5^2$$
$$VM = \sqrt{402.41}$$
$$= 20.06$$
$$= 20.1 \text{ cm} \quad \text{(correct to 3 sig. fig.)}$$

(e) Volume of the pyramid

$$= \frac{1}{3} \times (10 \times 10) \times 19.427$$
$$= 647.57$$
$$= 648 \text{ cm}^3 \quad \text{(correct to 3 sig. fig.)}$$

(f) Total surface area of pyramid

$$= 4 \times \text{area of } \triangle BCV + \text{area of base } ABCD$$
$$= 4 \times \frac{1}{2} \times 10 \times 20.06 + 10 \times 10$$
$$= 501 \text{ cm}^2 \quad \text{(correct to 3 sig. fig.)}$$

(g) In $\triangle MNV$,

$$\tan \angle VMN = \frac{VN}{MN}$$
$$= \frac{19.427}{5}$$
$$\angle VMN = 75.6° \quad \text{(correct to 1 d.p.)}$$

8. In the diagram, $ABCD$ is a horizontal rectangular field and TD is a vertical tower at D. The angle of intersection of AC and DB is 38°, and $AC = 100$ m.

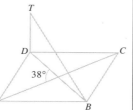

(a) Find the lengths of AB and BC.

(b) The angle of elevation of T from B is 25°. Find
   (i) the height of the tower,
   (ii) the angle of elevation of T from C.

Solution

(a) Let E be the point of intersection of AC and BD.

$$AE = BE \quad \text{(diagonals of a rectangle)}$$
$$\angle EAB = \angle EBA \quad \text{(base } \angle \text{s of isos. } \triangle)$$
$$\angle EAB + \angle EBA = 38° \quad \text{(ext. } \angle \text{ of } \triangle)$$
$$2\angle EAB = 38°$$
$$\angle EAB = 19°$$

In $\triangle ABC$,

$$\cos 19° = \frac{AB}{AC}$$
$$AB = 100 \cos 19°$$
$$= 94.552$$
$$= 94.6 \text{ m} \quad \text{(correct to 3 sig. fig.)}$$

$$\sin 19° = \frac{BC}{AC}$$
$$BC = 100 \sin 19°$$
$$= 32.557$$
$$= 32.6 \text{ m} \quad \text{(correct to 3 sig. fig.)}$$

(b) (i)
$$BD = AC \quad \text{(diagonals of rectangle)}$$
$$= 100 \text{ m}$$
In $\triangle BDT$,
$$\tan 25° = \frac{TD}{BD}$$
$$TD = 100 \tan 25°$$
$$= 46.631$$
$$= 46.6 \text{ m} \quad \text{(correct to 3 sig. fig.)}$$
The height of the tower is 46.6 m.

(ii) $CD = AB$ (opposite side of rectangle)
In $\triangle CDT$,

$$\tan \angle DCT = \frac{TD}{CD}$$
$$= \frac{46.631}{94.552}$$
$$\angle DCT = 26.3° \quad \text{(correct to 1 d.p.)}$$
The angle of elevation of T from C is 26.3°.

9. In the diagram, ACD is a triangular field on horizontal ground. B is a point on AC and TD is a vertical building. $AD = 80$ m, $BC = 53$ m, $\angle DAB = 60°$ and $\angle ABD = 45°$.

(a) Find the length of BD.

(b) Find the length of CD.

(c) If the angle of elevation of T from A is 37°, find
   (i) the height TD,
   (ii) the angle of elevation of the midpoint of TD from C.

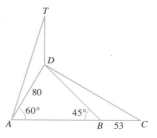

Solution

(a) In $\triangle ABD$, by the sine rule,

$$\frac{BD}{\sin 60°} = \frac{80}{\sin 45°}$$
$$BD = \frac{80 \sin 60°}{\sin 45°}$$
$$= 97.980$$
$$= 98.0 \text{ m} \quad \text{(correct to 3 sig. fig.)}$$

(b) In △BCD,

∠CBD = 180° − 45° (adj. ∠s on a st. line)

= 135°

By the cosine rule,

$CD^2 = 53^2 + 97.98^2 - 2 \times 53 \times 97.98$
$\times \cos 135°$

$CD = \sqrt{19\,753.0}$

= 140.55

= 141 m (correct to 3 sig. fig.)

(c) (i) In △ADT,

$\tan 37° = \dfrac{TD}{AD}$

$TD = 80 \tan 37°$

= 60.284

= 60.3 m (correct to 3 sig. fig.)

(ii) Let M be the midpoint of TD.

In △CDM,

$MD = \dfrac{1}{2}TD$

= 30.142 m

$\tan \angle DCM = \dfrac{MD}{CD}$

$= \dfrac{30.142}{140.55}$

∠DCM = 12.1° (correct to 1 d.p.)

The angle of elevation of M from C is 12.1°.

10. In the diagram, TC is a tower of height h m standing on horizontal ground ABC. A is due South of C and B is due East of C. The angles of elevation of T from A and B are 31° and 42° respectively, and AB = 95 m.

(a) Express the distances AC and BC in terms of h.

(b) Find the value of h.

(c) Find the bearing of A from B.

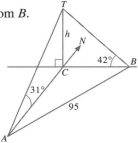

Solution

(a) In △ACT,

$\tan 31° = \dfrac{TC}{AC}$

$AC = \dfrac{h}{\tan 31°}$ m

In △BCT,

$\tan 42° = \dfrac{TC}{BC}$

$BC = \dfrac{h}{\tan 42°}$ m

(b) In △ABC,

$AC^2 + BC^2 = AB^2$
(Pythagoras' Theorem)

$\left(\dfrac{h}{\tan 31°}\right)^2 + \left(\dfrac{h}{\tan 42°}\right)^2 = 95^2$

$\left[\left(\dfrac{1}{\tan 31°}\right)^2 + \left(\dfrac{1}{\tan 42°}\right)^2\right]h^2 = 95^2$

$4.0033h^2 = 95^2$

$h = \sqrt{\dfrac{95^2}{4.0033}}$

= 47.480

= 47.5 (correct to 3 sig. fig.)

(c) In △ABC,

$\tan \angle ABC = \dfrac{AC}{AB}$

$= \dfrac{\dfrac{h}{\tan 31°}}{\dfrac{h}{\tan 42°}}$

$= \dfrac{\tan 42°}{\tan 31°}$

∠ABC = 56° (correct to the nearest degree)

Bearing of A from B = 270° − 56°

= 214°

Chapter 9   Coordinate Geometry

Class Activity 1

1.

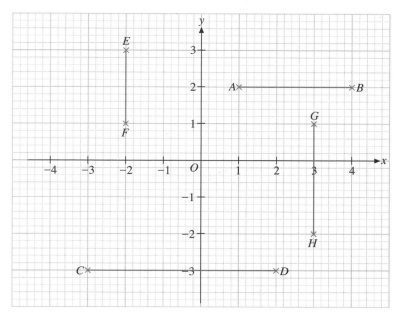

(a) The diagram shows 4 line segments, *AB*, *CD*, *EF* and *GH*. Copy and complete the following table for the lengths of the line segments.

Line Segment	Coordinates of end points	Length (units)
AB	A(1 , 2), B(4 , 2)	4 − 1 = 3
CD	C(−3 , −3), D(2 , −3)	2 − (−3) = 5
EF	E(−2 , 3), F(−2 , 1)	3 − 1 = 2
GH	G(3 , 1), H(3 , −2)	1 − (−2) = 3

(b) If the end points of a line segment are $A(x_1, k)$ and $B(x_2, k)$, where $x_2 > x_1$, what is the length of *AB?*

$x_2 - x_1$ units

(c) If the end points of a line segment are $C(h, y_1)$ and $D(h, y_2)$ where $y_2 > y_1$, what is the length of *CD?*

$y_2 - y_1$ units

81

2.

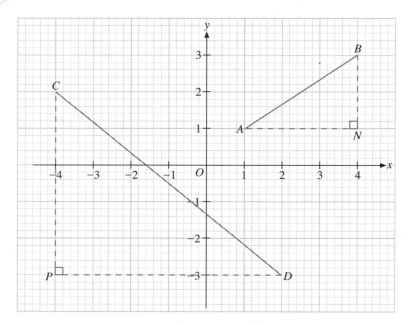

Find the lengths of line segments *AB* and *CD* in the above diagram by copying and completing the following.

The coordinates of *A*, *B* and *N* are
A(1 , 1), *B*(4 , 3) and *N*(4 , 1).

$AN = $ ____ 4 − 1 = 3 ____

$BN = $ ____ 3 − 1 = 2 ____

$AB^2 = AN^2 + BN^2$
          (Pythagoras' Theorem)

$= $ ____ $3^2 + 2^2$ ____

$\therefore\ AB = $ ____ $\sqrt{13}$ ____ units

The coordinates of *C*, *D* and *P* are
C(−4 , 2), *D*(2 , −3) and *P*(−4 , −3).

$CP = $ ____ 2 − (−3) = 5 ____

$DP = $ ____ 2 − (−4) = 6 ____

$CD^2 = $ ____ $CP^2 + DP^2$ ____

$= $ ____ $5^2 + 6^2$ ____

$\therefore\ CD = $ ____ $\sqrt{61}$ ____ units

Extend Your Learning Curve

Families of Straight Lines

Consider the equations

$$T : y = kx + 2,$$

$$P : y = \frac{3}{4}x + k,$$

and $F : (2x - y - 3) + k(x + 3y - 5) = 0.$

(a) For each equation, substitute *k* with several values and draw the corresponding graphs on the same diagram using a sheet of graph paper. (You should have three different diagrams, each for *T*, *P* and *F*.)

(b) Turn to the classmate next to you and compare your diagrams with those of your classmate's. Hence, write down your findings about these three equations of straight lines.

Solution

(a) $T : y = kx + 2$

$y = 2$ (i.e. $k = 0$)

x	-1	0	2
y	2	2	2

$y = x + 2$ (i.e. $k = 1$)

x	-2	0	2
y	0	2	4

$y = -x + 2$ (i.e. $k = -1$)

x	-2	0	2
y	4	2	0

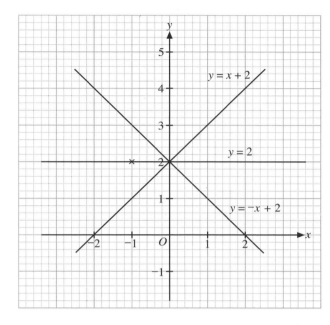

$P : y = \dfrac{3}{4}x + k$

$y = \dfrac{3}{4}x$ (i.e. $k = 0$)

x	-4	0	4
y	-3	0	3

$y = \dfrac{3}{4}x + 1$ (i.e. $k = 1$)

x	-4	0	4
y	-2	1	4

$y = \dfrac{3}{4}x - 2$ (i.e. $k = -2$)

x	-4	0	4
y	-5	-2	1

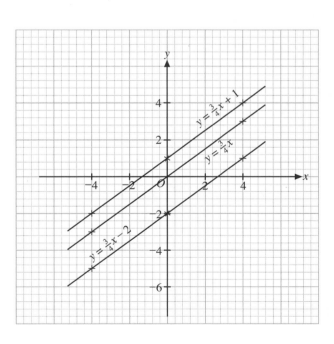

$F : (2x - y - 3) + k(x + 3y - 5) = 0$

When $k = 0$, the line is
$$2x - y - 3 = 0$$
i.e. $$y = 2x - 3.$$

When $k = 1$, the line is
$$2x - y - 3 + (x + 3y - 5) = 0$$
$$3x + 2y - 8 = 0$$
i.e. $$y = -\frac{3}{2}x + 4.$$

When $k = -2$, the line is
$$(2x - y - 3) - 2(x + 3y - 5) = 0$$
$$-7y + 7 = 0$$
i.e. $$y = 1.$$

$y = 2x - 3$

x	–2	0	4
y	–7	–3	5

$y = -\frac{3}{2}x + 4$

x	–2	0	4
y	7	4	–2

$y = 1$

x	–2	0	4
y	1	1	1

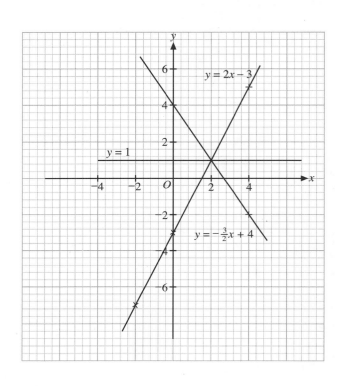

(b) Each member of the family $T : y = kx + 2$ has the y-intercept = 2. Each member of the family $P : y = \frac{3}{4}x + k$ has gradient $= \frac{3}{4}$. The members are parallel lines.

Each member of the family $F : (2x - y - 3) + k(x + 3y - 5) = 0$ passes through the point $(2, 1)$. In fact, $(2, 1)$ is the point of intersection of the lines $2x - y - 3 = 0$ and $x + 3y - 5 = 0$.

Try It!

Section 9.1

1. Three points are $P(-7, -4)$, $Q(-4, -2)$ and $R(2, 2)$.
   (a) Find the lengths of PQ, QR and PR.
   (b) Show that P, Q and R lie on a straight line.

Solution
(a) $PQ = \sqrt{(-4+7)^2 + (-2+4)^2}$

   $= \sqrt{9+4}$

   $= \sqrt{13}$

   $= 3.61$ units

   $QR = \sqrt{(2+4)^2 + (2+2)^2}$

   $= \sqrt{36+16}$

   $= \sqrt{52}$

   $= 7.21$ units

   $PR = \sqrt{(2+7)^2 + (2+4)^2}$

   $= \sqrt{81+36}$

   $= \sqrt{117}$

   $= 10.82$ units

(b) $PQ + QR = 3.61 + 7.21$

   $= 10.82$

   $\therefore PQ + QR = PR$

   Hence, P, Q and R lie on a straight line.

2. The vertices of $\triangle PQR$ are $P(3, 2)$, $Q(-3, 0)$ and $R(4, -1)$.
   (a) Find the lengths of PQ, QR and RP.
   (b) Show that $\triangle PQR$ is a right-angled triangle.
   (c) Find the perimeter of $\triangle PQR$, correct to 3 significant figures.
   (d) Find the area of $\triangle PQR$.

Solution
(a) $PQ = \sqrt{(-3-3)^2 + (0-2)^2}$

   $= \sqrt{40}$ units

   $QR = \sqrt{(4+3)^2 + (-1-0)^2}$

   $= \sqrt{50}$ units

   $RP = \sqrt{(4-3)^2 + (-1-2)^2}$

   $= \sqrt{10}$ units

(b) $PQ^2 + RP^2 = 40 + 10$

   $= 50$

   $\therefore PQ^2 + RP^2 = QR^2$

   $\therefore \angle QPR = 90°$

   (converse of Pythagoras' Theorem)

   i.e. $\triangle PQR$ is a right-angled triangle.

(c) Perimeter of $\triangle PQR$

   $= \sqrt{40} + \sqrt{50} + \sqrt{10}$

   $= 16.6$ units   (correct to 3 sig. fig.)

(d) Area of $\triangle PQR = \frac{1}{2} \times PQ \times RP$

   $= \frac{1}{2} \times (\sqrt{40}) \times (\sqrt{10})$

   $= 10$ units^2

Section 9.2

3. Find the gradient of the line joining the points
   (a) $P(-4, 1)$ and $Q(3, 5)$,
   (b) $R(0, -3)$ and $S(4, 2)$.

Solution
(a) Gradient of $PQ = \dfrac{5-1}{3-(-4)}$

   $= \dfrac{4}{7}$

(b) Gradient of $RS = \dfrac{2-(-3)}{4-0}$

   $= \dfrac{5}{4}$

4. The line joining the points $Q(-2, 3)$ and $R(6, -1)$ intersects the x-axis at T.
   (a) Find the gradient of the line.
   (b) Find the coordinates of T.

Solution
(a) Gradient of $QR = \dfrac{3-(-1)}{-2-6}$

   $= \dfrac{4}{-8}$

   $= -\dfrac{1}{2}$

(b) Let $(t, 0)$ be the coordinates of T.
   Gradient of QT = gradient of QR

   $\dfrac{0-3}{t-(-2)} = -\dfrac{1}{2}$

   $6 = t + 2$

   $t = 4$

   i.e. the coordinates of T are $(4, 0)$.

5. Find the gradient of the line
   (a) $y = 1$,
   (b) $x = -3$.

Solution
(a) $y = 1$ is a horizontal line.
   $\therefore$ its gradient is 0.
(b) $x = -3$ is a vertical line.
   $\therefore$ its gradient is undefined.

Section 9.3

6. Find the equation of the line

   (a) L_3 with gradient $= \frac{2}{5}$ and passing through the origin,

   (b) L_4 with gradient $= -\frac{1}{2}$ and passing through the point $B(4, 1)$.

Solution

(a) y-intercept $= 0$

   gradient $= \frac{2}{5}$

   $\therefore$ the equation of L_3 is

   $$y = \frac{2}{5}x + 0$$

   i.e. $y = \frac{2}{5}x.$

(b) Let the equation of L_4 be $y = -\frac{1}{2}x + c.$

   Since $B(4, 1)$ is on L_4, $\quad 1 = -\frac{1}{2}(4) + c$

   $$c = 3$$

   Hence, the equation of L_4 is $y = -\frac{1}{2}x + 3.$

7. Find the equation of the line
   (a) L_3 that passes through the points $P(-2, 3)$ and $Q(2, -1)$,
   (b) L_4 that passes through the points $R(-4, 5)$ and $S(-1, 5)$.

Solution

(a) Gradient of $L_3 =$ gradient of PQ

   $$= \frac{-1 - 3}{2 - (-2)}$$

   $$= -1$$

   Let the equation of L_3 be $y = -x + c.$
   Since $P(-2, 3)$ is on L_3, $\quad 3 = -(-2) + c$

   $$c = 1$$

   $\therefore$ the equation of L_3 is $y = -x + 1.$

(b) Gradient of $L_4 =$ gradient of RS

   $$= \frac{5 - 5}{-1 - (-4)}$$

   $$= 0$$

   $\therefore$ L_4 is a horizontal line.
   Since it passes through $R(-4, 5)$, the equation of L_4 is $y = 5.$

8. The equation of a straight line L is $2x - 3y + 4 = 0.$
   (a) Express the equation in the gradient-intercept form.
   (b) Hence state the gradient and the y-intercept of L.

Solution

(a) $L: 2x - 3y + 4 = 0$

   $$3y = 2x + 4$$

   Hence, the gradient-intercept form is $y = \frac{2}{3}x + \frac{4}{3}.$

(b) Gradient of $L = \frac{2}{3}$

   y-intercept of $L = \frac{4}{3}$

Exercise 9.1
Basic Practice

1. In each of following, find the length of the line segment with the given end points.
   - **(a)** $A(3, 2)$, $B(7, 2)$
   - **(b)** $C(4, 5)$, $D(4, -3)$
   - **(c)** $O(0, 0)$, $E(-3, 4)$
   - **(d)** $G(3, 1)$, $H(8, 13)$
   - **(e)** $K(-2, 5)$, $L(-7, 6)$
   - **(f)** $P(4, -3)$, $Q(-1, -7)$

Solution

(a) $AB = \sqrt{(7-3)^2 + (2-2)^2}$
$= 4$ units

(b) $CD = \sqrt{(4-4)^2 + (-3-5)^2}$
$= 8$ units

(c) $OE = \sqrt{(-3-0)^2 + (4-0)^2}$
$= 5$ units

(d) $GH = \sqrt{(8-3)^2 + (13-1)^2}$
$= 13$ units

(e) $KL = \sqrt{(-7+2)^2 + (6-5)^2}$
$= \sqrt{26}$ units

(f) $PQ = \sqrt{(-1-4)^2 + (-7+3)^2}$
$= \sqrt{41}$ units

2. $A(1, 3)$ and $B(2, 6)$ are points on a coordinate plane.
   - **(a)** Find the lengths of the line segments OA, OB and AB, where O is the origin.
   - **(b)** Show that the points O, A and B lie on a straight line.
   - **(c)** What is the relationship between the point A and the line segment OB?

Solution

(a) $OA = \sqrt{(1-0)^2 + (3-0)^2}$
$= \sqrt{10}$ units

$OB = \sqrt{(2-0)^2 + (6-0)^2}$
$= \sqrt{40}$ units

$AB = \sqrt{(2-1)^2 + (6-3)^2}$
$= \sqrt{10}$ units

(b) $OA + AB = \sqrt{10} + \sqrt{10}$
$= 2\sqrt{10}$
$= \sqrt{40}$ units
$\therefore\ OA + AB = OB$
Hence, O, A and B lie on a straight line.

(c) Since $OA = AB$, A is the midpoint of OB.

Further Practice

3. In each of the following,
   - **(i)** find the lengths of AB, BC and CA,
   - **(ii)** determine whether the points A, B and C lie on a straight line.
   - **(a)** $A(-4, 3)$, $B(-2, 2)$, $C(0, 1)$
   - **(b)** $A(-3, -2)$, $B(1, -1)$, $C(3, 0)$

Solution

(a) (i) $AB = \sqrt{(-2+4)^2 + (2-3)^2}$
$= \sqrt{5}$ units

$BC = \sqrt{(0+2)^2 + (1-2)^2}$
$= \sqrt{5}$ units

$CA = \sqrt{(0+4)^2 + (1-3)^2}$
$= \sqrt{20}$ units

(ii) $AB + BC = \sqrt{5} + \sqrt{5}$
$= 2\sqrt{5}$
$= \sqrt{20}$ units
$\therefore\ AB + BC = CA$
Hence, A, B and C lie on a straight line.

(b) (i) $AB = \sqrt{(1+3)^2 + (-1+2)^2}$
$= \sqrt{17}$ units

$BC = \sqrt{(3-1)^2 + (0+1)^2}$
$= \sqrt{5}$ units

$CA = \sqrt{(3+3)^2 + (0+2)^2}$
$= \sqrt{40}$ units

(ii) Since $AB + BC = \sqrt{17} + \sqrt{5} \neq CA$, A, B and C do not lie on the same straight line.

4. The vertices of $\triangle ABC$ are $A(-2, -1)$, $B(2, -1)$ and $C(1, 3)$.
   - **(a)** Find the lengths of AB, BC and CA.
   - **(b)** Find the perimeter of $\triangle ABC$.
   - **(c)** Find the area of $\triangle ABC$.

Solution

(a) $AB = \sqrt{(2+2)^2 + (-1+1)^2}$
$= 4$ units

$BC = \sqrt{(1-2)^2 + (3+1)^2}$
$= \sqrt{17}$ units

$CA = \sqrt{(1+2)^2 + (3+1)^2}$
$= 5$ units

(b) Perimeter of $\triangle ABC$

$$= 4 + \sqrt{17} + 5$$
$$= 13.1 \text{ units} \quad \text{(correct to 3 sig. fig.)}$$

(c) AB is horizontal.

Distance from C to $AB = 3 + 1 = 4$

$\therefore$ area of $\triangle ABC = \dfrac{1}{2} \times 4 \times 4$

$$= 8 \text{ units}^2$$

5. The vertices of $\triangle PQR$ are $P(-4, 4)$, $Q(5, 2)$, and $R(4, 6)$.
   (a) Find the lengths of PQ, QR and RP.
   (b) Find the perimeter of $\triangle PQR$.
   (c) Show that $\triangle PQR$ is a right-angled triangle.
   (d) Find the area of $\triangle PQR$.

Solution

(a) $PQ = \sqrt{(5 + 4)^2 + (2 - 4)^2}$

$$= \sqrt{85} \text{ units}$$

$QR = \sqrt{(4 - 5)^2 + (6 - 2)^2}$

$$= \sqrt{17} \text{ units}$$

$RP = \sqrt{(4 + 4)^2 + (6 - 4)^2}$

$$= \sqrt{68} \text{ units}$$

(b) Perimeter of $\triangle PQR$
$$= \sqrt{85} + \sqrt{17} + \sqrt{68} \text{ units}$$
$$= 21.6 \text{ units} \quad \text{(correct to 3 sig. fig.)}$$

(c) $QR^2 + RP^2 = 17 + 68$
$$= 85$$
$$= PQ^2$$
$\therefore \ \angle PRQ = 90°$ (converse of Pythagoras' Theorem)
i.e. $\triangle PQR$ is a right-angled triangle.

(d) Area of $\triangle PQR = \dfrac{1}{2} \times \sqrt{68} \times \sqrt{17}$
$$= 17 \text{ units}^2$$

6. The distance between the points $P(-3, 2)$ and $Q(1, k)$ is 5. Find the possible values of k.

Solution

$$PQ = 5$$
$$(1 + 3)^2 + (k - 2)^2 = 5^2$$
$$(k - 2)^2 = 9$$
$$k - 2 = -3 \text{ or } 3$$
$$k = -1 \text{ or } 5$$

7. $A(4, 7)$ and $B(-3, 2)$ are points on a coordinate plane. Find the coordinates of a point C on the x-axis such that $AC = BC$.

Solution

Let the coordinates of C be $(c, 0)$.
$$AC = BC$$
$$(c - 4)^2 + (0 - 7)^2 = (c + 3)^2 + (0 - 2)^2$$
$$c^2 - 8c + 16 + 49 = c^2 + 6c + 9 + 4$$
$$14c = 52$$
$$c = \frac{26}{7}$$

$\therefore$ the coordinates of C are $\left(\dfrac{26}{7}, 0\right)$.

Maths@Work

8. In the diagram, AOC and BOD are straight lines.
   (a) Find the lengths of OA, OB, OC and OD.
   (b) Name a triangle which is congruent to $\triangle AOB$ and state the reason for the congruence.
   (c) Find the area of $\triangle OCD$.

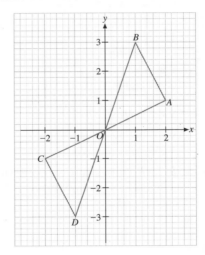

Solution
(a) The coordinates of A, B, C and D are $(2, 1)$, $(1, 3)$, $(-2, -1)$ and $(-1, -3)$ respectively.

$OA = \sqrt{(2 - 0)^2 + (1 - 0)^2}$

$$= \sqrt{5} \text{ units}$$

$OB = \sqrt{(1 - 0)^2 + (3 - 0)^2}$

$$= \sqrt{10} \text{ units}$$

$OC = \sqrt{(-2 - 0)^2 + (-1 - 0)^2}$

$$= \sqrt{5} \text{ units}$$

$OD = \sqrt{(-1 - 0)^2 + (-3 - 0)^2}$

$$= \sqrt{10} \text{ units}$$

(b) In $\triangle AOB$ and $\triangle COD$,
$$OA = OC \qquad \text{(proved)}$$
$$\angle AOB = \angle COD \qquad \text{(vert. opp. } \angle\text{s)}$$
$$OB = OD \qquad \text{(proved)}$$
$\therefore \ \triangle AOB \equiv \triangle COD$ (SAS)

(c) Draw perpendiculars *CN* and *DM* from the points *C* and *D* to the *x*-axis.

$$\text{Area of } \triangle ODM = \frac{1}{2} \times 1 \times 3$$
$$= \frac{3}{2} \text{ units}^2$$
$$\text{Area of trapezium } CNMD = \frac{1}{2} \times (1 \times 3) \times 1$$
$$= 2 \text{ units}^2$$
$$\text{Area of } \triangle OCN = \frac{1}{2} \times 1 \times 2$$
$$= 1 \text{ unit}^2$$
$$\text{Area of } \triangle OCD = \frac{3}{2} + 2 - 1$$
$$= 2\frac{1}{2} \text{ units}^2$$

9. The vertices of a parallelogram *ABCD* are *A*(5, 4), *B*(−3, 2), *C*(−4, −3) and *D*(4, −1).
(a) Draw the diagram of *ABCD* on a coordinate plane.
(b) Show that *AB* = *DC* and *AD* = *BC* by finding the lengths of the sides.
(c) Find the perimeter of *ABCD*.

Solution
(a)
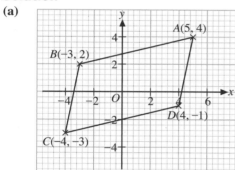

(b)
$$AB = \sqrt{(-3-5)^2 + (2-4)^2}$$
$$= \sqrt{68} \text{ units}$$
$$DC = \sqrt{(-4-4)^2 + (-3+1)^2}$$
$$= \sqrt{68} \text{ units}$$
$$\therefore AB = DC$$
$$AD = \sqrt{(4-5)^2 + (-1-4)^2}$$
$$= \sqrt{26} \text{ units}$$
$$BC = \sqrt{(-4+3)^2 + (-3-2)^2}$$
$$= \sqrt{26} \text{ units}$$
$$\therefore AD = BC$$

(c) Perimeter of *ABCD*
$$= 2(\sqrt{68} + \sqrt{26})$$
$$= 26.7 \text{ units} \quad \text{(correct to 3 sig. fig.)}$$

10. In the diagram, *OABC* is a rectangle in which *O* is the origin and the vertices *A* and *C* are *A*(*a*, 0) and *C*(0, *c*).
(a) Express the coordinates of *B* in terms of *a* and *c*.
(b) Show that *OB* = *AC* by finding the lengths of these two diagonals.
(c) Let *P*(*s*, *t*) be any point inside the rectangle. Prove that $OP^2 + BP^2 = AP^2 + CP^2$.

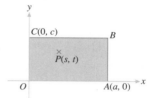

Solution
(a) The coordinates of *B* are (*a*, *c*).
(b)
$$OB = \sqrt{(a-0)^2 + (c-0)^2}$$
$$= \sqrt{a^2 + c^2} \text{ units}$$
$$AC = \sqrt{(0-a)^2 + (c-0)^2}$$
$$= \sqrt{a^2 + c^2} \text{ units}$$
$$\therefore OB = AC$$
(c)
$$OP^2 + BP^2 = (s-0)^2 + (t-0)^2 + (s-a)^2 + (t-c)^2$$
$$= s^2 + t^2 + (s-a)^2 + (t-c)^2$$
$$AP^2 + CP^2 = (s-a)^2 + (t-0)^2 + (s-0)^2 + (t-c)^2$$
$$= s^2 + t^2 + (s-a)^2 + (t-c)^2$$
$$\therefore OP^2 + BP^2 = AP^2 + CP^2$$

Brainworks
11. Given a point *G*(1, 2), find the coordinates of two possible positions of a point *P*(*a*, *b*) in the second quadrant such that the length of *PG* = 5 units.

Solution
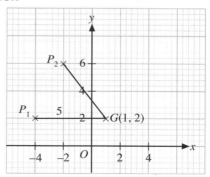

In the diagram, two possible coordinates of P are $P_1(-4, 2)$ and $P_2(-2, 6)$.

$P_1G = \sqrt{(1+4)^2 + (2-2)^2}$
$= 5$ units

$P_2G = \sqrt{(1+2)^2 + (2-6)^2}$
$= 5$ units

Exercise 9.2
Basic Practice

1. In each of the following, find the gradient of the line passing through the given pair of points.
   (a) $A(3, 4)$, $B(6, 7)$
   (b) $C(-5, 8)$, $D(-2, 5)$
   (c) $E(2, 3)$, $F(2, -5)$
   (d) $G(-7, -1)$, $H(3, -1)$

   Solution

   (a) Gradient of $AB = \dfrac{7-4}{6-3}$
   $= 1$

   (b) Gradient of $CD = \dfrac{5-8}{-2-(-5)}$
   $= -1$

   (c) Gradient of $EF = \dfrac{-5-3}{2-2}$
   $= \dfrac{-8}{0}$
   $\therefore$ gradient of EF is undefined.

   (d) Gradient of $GH = \dfrac{-1-(-1)}{3-(-7)}$
   $= 0$

2. Find the gradients of the line segments AB, CD, EF and GH in the diagram.

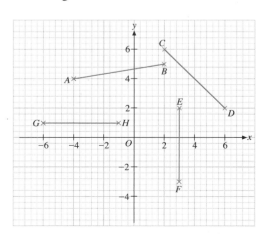

Solution

Gradient of $AB = \dfrac{5-4}{2-(-4)}$
$= \dfrac{1}{6}$

Gradient of $CD = \dfrac{2-6}{6-2}$
$= -1$

Since EF is vertical, gradient of EF is undefined.

Gradient of $GH = \dfrac{1-1}{-1-(-6)}$
$= 0$

3. The vertices of $\triangle ABC$ are $A(-5, -3)$, $B(4, 0)$ and $C(-1, 3)$. Find the gradients of the sides of the triangle.

Solution

Gradient of $AB = \dfrac{0+3}{4+5}$
$= \dfrac{1}{3}$

Gradient of $BC = \dfrac{3-0}{-1-4}$
$= -\dfrac{3}{5}$

Gradient of $CA = \dfrac{-3-3}{-5-(-1)}$
$= \dfrac{3}{2}$

Further Practice

4. The gradient of the line passing through $A(2, 3)$ and $B(k, 7)$ is $\dfrac{2}{3}$. Find the value of k.

Solution

Gradient of $AB = \dfrac{2}{3}$
$\dfrac{7-3}{k-2} = \dfrac{2}{3}$
$12 = 2k - 4$
$2k = 16$
$k = 8$

5. The points $A(-5, -3)$, $B(-2, k)$ and $C(4, 3)$ lie on a straight line. Find the value of k.

Solution

Gradient of AB = gradient of AC
$\dfrac{k-(-3)}{-2-(-5)} = \dfrac{3-(-3)}{4-(-5)}$
$\dfrac{k+3}{3} = \dfrac{2}{3}$
$k + 3 = 2$
$k = -1$

6. The line segment joining $P(-6, 7)$ and $Q(5, -2)$ intersects the y-axis at the point R. Find the coordinates of R.

Solution

Let the coordinates of R be $(0, r)$.
Gradient of PR = gradient of PQ

$$\frac{r - 7}{0 - (-6)} = \frac{-2 - 7}{5 - (-6)}$$

$$\frac{r - 7}{6} = \frac{-9}{11}$$

$$11r - 77 = -54$$

$$11r = 23$$

$$r = \frac{23}{11}$$

$\therefore$ the coordinates of R are $\left(0, \frac{23}{11}\right)$.

Maths@Work

7. The vertices of a parallelogram $ABCD$ are $A(-2, -2)$, $B(2, -1)$, $C(3, 2)$ and $D(-1, 1)$.
  (a) Find the gradients of all 4 sides of $ABCD$.
  (b) What can you say about the gradients of the opposite sides of a parallelogram?

Solution

(a) Gradient of $AB = \dfrac{-1 - (-2)}{2 - (-2)}$

$\qquad\qquad = \dfrac{1}{4}$

Gradient of $BC = \dfrac{2 - (-1)}{3 - 2}$

$\qquad\qquad = 3$

Gradient of $CD = \dfrac{1 - 2}{-1 - 3}$

$\qquad\qquad = \dfrac{1}{4}$

Gradient of $DA = \dfrac{1 - (-2)}{-1 - (-2)}$

$\qquad\qquad = 3$

(b) From **(a)**, we have
$\qquad$ gradient of AB = gradient of CD,
and $\quad$ gradient of BC = gradient of DA.
$\therefore$ the gradients of opposite sides of a parallelogram are equal.

8. The vertices of a rectangle $PQRS$ are $P(-2, -3)$, $Q(4, 0)$, $R(2, 4)$ and $S(-4, 1)$.
  (a) Find the gradients of all 4 sides of $PQRS$.
  (b) What can you say about the gradients of the adjacent sides of a rectangle?

Solution

(a) Gradient of $PQ = \dfrac{0 - (-3)}{4 - (-2)}$

$\qquad\qquad = \dfrac{1}{2}$

Gradient of $QR = \dfrac{4 - 0}{2 - 4}$

$\qquad\qquad = -2$

Gradient of $RS = \dfrac{1 - 4}{-4 - 2}$

$\qquad\qquad = \dfrac{1}{2}$

Gradient of $SP = \dfrac{-3 - 1}{-2 - (-4)}$

$\qquad\qquad = -2$

(b) Gradient of PQ × gradient of $QR = \dfrac{1}{2} \times (-2)$

$\qquad\qquad\qquad\qquad\qquad\qquad = -1$

The product of the gradients of adjacent sides of a rectangle is equal to -1.

9. In the diagram, a vertical pole OP is supported by two wires, AB and AC, of equal lengths. The gradient of AB is $\dfrac{4}{3}$ and the coordinates of B are $(-75, 0)$, where the unit of length in the coordinate system is cm.
  (a) Find the coordinates of the point A.
  (b) Find the length of AB.
  (c) Find the coordinates of the point C.
  (d) Find the gradient of AC.

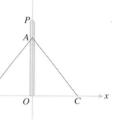

Solution

(a) Let the coordinates of A be $(0, a)$.

$\qquad$ Gradient of $AB = \dfrac{4}{3}$

$$\frac{a - 0}{0 - (-75)} = \frac{4}{3}$$

$$\frac{a}{75} = \frac{4}{3}$$

$$a = 100$$

$\therefore$ the coordinates of A are $(0, 100)$.

(b) $AB = \sqrt{(-75 - 0)^2 + (0 - 100)^2}$

$\qquad\quad = 125$ cm

(c) The points B and C are symmetrical about the y-axis.
$\qquad \therefore$ the coordinates of C are $(75, 0)$.

(d) Gradient of $AC = \dfrac{0 - 100}{75 - 0}$

$\qquad\qquad\qquad = -\dfrac{4}{3}$

10. In the diagram, *OABC* is a rhombus, where *O* is the origin. The coordinates of *A* and *C* are (*a*, 0) and (*s*, *t*) respectively.
    (a) Write down the coordinates of *B* in terms of *a*, *s* and *t*.
    (b) Find the length of *OC* in terms of *s* and *t*.
    (c) State a relationship between *a*, *s* and *t*.
    (d) Express in terms of *a*, *s* and *t*
        (i) the gradient of *OB*,
        (ii) the gradient of *AC*.
    (e) Show that the product of the gradients of *OB* and *AC* is −1.

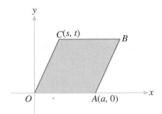

Solution
(a) The coordinates of *B* are (*a* + *s*, *t*).

(b) $OC = \sqrt{(s-0)^2 + (t-0)^2}$
    $= \sqrt{s^2 + t^2}$ units

(c) Since *OABC* is a rhombus, *OA* = *OC*.
    $\therefore \quad a = \sqrt{s^2 + t^2}$
    Hence, $a^2 = s^2 + t^2$

(d) (i) Gradient of $OB = \dfrac{t-0}{(a+s)-0}$
        $= \dfrac{t}{a+s}$

    (ii) Gradient of $AC = \dfrac{t-0}{s-a}$
        $= \dfrac{t}{s-a}$

(e) Gradient of *OB* × gradient of *AC*
    $= \dfrac{t}{a+s} \times \dfrac{t}{s-a}$
    $= \dfrac{t^2}{s^2 - a^2}$
    $= \dfrac{t^2}{s^2 - (s^2 + t^2)}$ (from (c))
    $= \dfrac{t^2}{-t^2}$
    $= -1$

Brainworks

11. Given a point *P*(4, −2), find two possible pairs of coordinates of a point *Q* such that the gradient of *PQ* is $-\dfrac{3}{5}$.

Solution

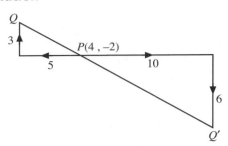

The coordinates of *Q* can be located as shown in the above diagram.

For instance, move 5 units to the left from *P* and then 3 units upwards to *Q*(−1, 1).
Gradient of $PQ = \dfrac{1-(-2)}{-1-4}$
$= -\dfrac{3}{5}$

Alternatively, move 10 units to the right from *P* and then 6 units down to *Q*′(14, −8).
Gradient of $PQ' = \dfrac{-8-(-2)}{14-4}$
$= -\dfrac{3}{5}$

Exercise 9.3
Basic Practice

1. For each of the following, write down the equation of the line given its gradient *m* and *y*-intercept *c*.
    (a) $m = 2, c = 3$ (b) $m = -\dfrac{2}{7}, c = 7$
    (c) $m = -3, c = -5$ (d) $m = \dfrac{4}{9}, c = 0$

    Solution
    (a) The equation of the line is $y = 2x + 3$.
    (b) The equation of the line is $y = -\dfrac{2}{7}x + 7$.
    (c) The equation of the line is $y = -3x - 5$.
    (d) The equation of the line is $y = \dfrac{4}{9}x + 0$.
        i.e. $y = \dfrac{4}{9}x$.

2. For each of the following, write down the equation of the line that passes through the given point *A* and has gradient *m*.
    (a) $m = 3, A(1, 4)$
    (b) $m = -2, A(3, -5)$
    (c) $m = 0, A(-3, 4)$
    (d) $m = -\dfrac{4}{5}, A(-2, -7)$

Solution

(a) Let the equation of the line be $y = 3x + c$.
Since $A(1, 4)$ is on the line, $4 = 3(1) + c$
$$c = 1$$
∴ the equation of the line is $y = 3x + 1$.

(b) Let the equation of the line be $y = -2x + d$.
Since $A(3, -5)$ is on the line, $-5 = -2(3) + d$
$$d = 1$$
∴ the equation of the line is $y = -2x + 1$.

(c) Let the equation of the line be $y = 0x + h$,
i.e. $y = h$.
Since $A(-3, 4)$ is on the line, $4 = 0(-3) + h$
$$h = 4$$
∴ the equation of the line is $y = 4$.

(d) Let the equation of the line be $y = -\dfrac{4}{5}x + k$.

Since $A(-2, -7)$ is on the line, $-7 = -\dfrac{4}{5}(-2) + k$

$$k = -\frac{43}{5}$$

∴ the equation of the line is $y = -\dfrac{4}{5}x - \dfrac{43}{5}$.

3. Write down the equation of the line that passes through the two given points A and B.
(a) $A(-3, 5)$, $B(0, 7)$
(b) $A(-3, -2)$, $B(2, -3)$
(c) $A(4, 3)$, $B(4, 9)$
(d) $A(-5, -6)$, $B(8, -6)$

Solution

(a) Gradient of $AB = \dfrac{7 - 5}{0 - (-3)}$

$$= \frac{2}{3}$$

Let the equation of the line be $y = \dfrac{2}{3}x + c$.

Since $B(0, 7)$ is on the line, $7 = \dfrac{2}{3}(0) + c$

$$c = 7$$

∴ the equation of the line is $y = \dfrac{2}{3}x + 7$.

(b) Gradient of $AB = \dfrac{-3 - (-2)}{2 - (-3)}$

$$= -\frac{1}{5}$$

Let the equation of the line be $y = -\dfrac{1}{5}x + d$.

Since $B(2, -3)$ is on the line, $-3 = -\dfrac{1}{5}(2) + d$

$$d = -\frac{13}{5}$$

∴ the equation of the line is $y = -\dfrac{1}{5}x - \dfrac{13}{5}$.

(c) Gradient of $AB = \dfrac{9 - 3}{4 - 4}$

$$= \frac{6}{0}$$

∴ gradient of AB is undefined.
AB is a vertical line.
Since $A(4, 3)$ is on the line, the equation of AB is $x = 4$.

(d) Gradient of $AB = \dfrac{-6 - (-6)}{8 - (-5)}$

$$= 0$$

∴ AB is a horizontal line.
Since $A(-5, -6)$ is on the line, the equation of the line is $y = -6$.

4. For each of the following equations,
(i) express it in the gradient-intercept form,
(ii) write down the gradient and the y-intercept of the line.
(a) $2x + y - 3 = 0$ **(b)** $x - 4y - 8 = 0$
(c) $3x + 7y + 6 = 0$ **(d)** $\dfrac{x}{5} + \dfrac{y}{3} = 1$

Solution

(a) **(i)** $2x + y - 3 = 0$
∴ the gradient-intercept form is
$y = -2x + 3$.

(ii) Gradient of the line $= -2$
y-intercept of the line $= 3$

(b) **(i)** $x - 4y - 8 = 0$
$$4y = x - 8$$
∴ $y = \dfrac{1}{4}x - 2$

is the gradient-intercept form of the line.

(ii) Gradient of the line $= \dfrac{1}{4}$
y-intercept of the line $= -2$

(c) **(i)** $3x + 7y + 6 = 0$
$$7y = -3x - 6$$
∴ $y = -\dfrac{3}{7}x - \dfrac{6}{7}$

is the gradient-intercept form of the line.

(ii) Gradient of the line $= -\dfrac{3}{7}$

y-intercept of the line $= -\dfrac{6}{7}$

(d) **(i)** $\dfrac{x}{5} + \dfrac{y}{3} = 1$

$$\frac{y}{3} = -\frac{x}{5} + 1$$

∴ $y = -\dfrac{3}{5}x + 3$

is the gradient-intercept form of the line.

(ii) Gradient of the line $= -\dfrac{3}{5}$

y-intercept of the line $= 3$

Further Practice

5. Find the equations of the lines L_1, L_2, L_3, L_4 and L_5 in the following diagram.

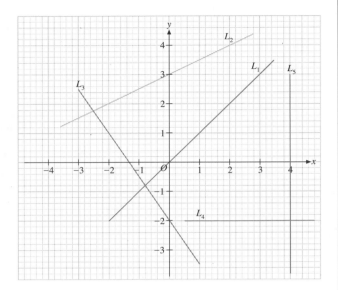

Solution

The line L_1 passes through $(0, 0)$ and $(3, 3)$.

Gradient of $L_1 = \dfrac{3-0}{3-0}$

$= 1$

y-intercept of $L_1 = 0$

$\therefore$ the equation of L_1 is $y = x$.

The line L_2 passes through $(0, 3)$ and $(2, 4)$.

Gradient of $L_2 = \dfrac{4-3}{2-0}$

$= \dfrac{1}{2}$

y-intercept $= 3$

$\therefore$ the equation of L_2 is $y = \dfrac{1}{2}x + 3$.

The line L_3 passes through $(0, -2)$ and $(-2, 1)$.

Gradient of $L_3 = \dfrac{1-(-2)}{-2-0}$

$= -\dfrac{3}{2}$

y-intercept $= -2$

$\therefore$ the equation of L_3 is $y = -\dfrac{3}{2}x - 2$.

L_4 is a horizontal line that passes through $(1, -2)$.
The equation of L_4 is $y = -2$.
L_5 is a vertical line that passes through $(4, 0)$.
The equation of L_5 is $x = 4$.

6. A line L cuts the x-axis at $A(4, 0)$ and the y-axis at $B(0, -3)$. Find
   (a) the gradient of the line L,
   (b) the equation of the line L,
   (c) the area of $\triangle OAB$, where O is the origin,
   (d) the length of AB,
   (e) the perpendicular distance from O to L.

Solution

(a) Gradient of $L = \dfrac{-3-0}{0-4}$

$= \dfrac{3}{4}$

(b) Since y-intercept of $L = -3$, the equation of the line L is $y = \dfrac{3}{4}x - 3$.

(c) Area of $\triangle OAB = \dfrac{1}{2} \times OA \times OB$

$= \dfrac{1}{2} \times 4 \times 3$

$= 6 \text{ units}^2$

(d) $AB = \sqrt{(0-4)^2 + (-3-0)^2}$

$= 5 \text{ units}$

(e) Let h units be the perpendicular distance from O to the line L.

Area of $\triangle DAB = \dfrac{1}{2} \times AB \times h$

$= \dfrac{1}{2} \times 5 \times h$

$\therefore \quad \dfrac{1}{2} \times 5 \times h = 6$

$h = \dfrac{12}{5}$

$\therefore$ the required distance is $2\dfrac{2}{5}$ units.

7. The gradient of the line $6x + ky - 9 = 0$ is $-\dfrac{3}{4}$. Find
   (a) the value of k,
   (b) the y-intercept of the line.

Solution

(a) $6x + ky - 9 = 0$

$ky = -6x + 9$

$y = -\dfrac{6}{k}x + \dfrac{9}{k}$

$\therefore$ gradient $= -\dfrac{6}{k}$

$= -\dfrac{3}{4}$

Hence, $k = 8$

(b) y-intercept of the line $= \dfrac{9}{k}$

$= \dfrac{9}{8}$

8. A line L_1 passes through $A(2, -5)$. The gradient of L_1 is equal to that of the line L_2: $3x - 7y + 6 = 0$. Find the equation of L_1.

Solution

L_2: $3x - 7y + 6 = 0$

$$7y = 3x + 6$$

$$y = \frac{3}{7}x + \frac{6}{7}$$

$\therefore$ gradient of $L_2 = \frac{3}{7}$.

Hence, gradient of $L_1 = \frac{3}{7}$.

Let the equation of L_1 be $y = \frac{3}{7}x + c$.

Since $A(2, -5)$ is on L_1, $\quad -5 = \frac{3}{7}(2) + c$

$$c = -\frac{41}{7}$$

$\therefore$ the equation of L_1 is $y = \frac{3}{7}x - \frac{41}{7}$.

9. The gradient of a line L_1 is $-\frac{4}{5}$. It cuts the y-axis at the same point as the line L_2: $7x + 4y - 12 = 0$. Find the equation of L_1.

Solution

L_2: $7x + 4y - 12 = 0$

$$4y = -7x + 12$$

$$y = -\frac{7}{4}x + 3$$

$\therefore$ y-intercept of L_1 = y-intercept of L_2
$$= 3$$

Hence, the equation of L_1 is $y = -\frac{4}{5}x + 3$.

Maths@Work

10. The vertices of $\triangle ABC$ are $A(-4, 1)$, $B(-4, -2)$ and $C(2, 5)$. Find
    (a) the equations of the lines AB, BC and CA,
    (b) the coordinates of the point where AC cuts the y-axis,
    (c) the area of $\triangle ABC$,
    (d) the perpendicular distance from A to BC.

Solution

(a) Gradient of $AB = \dfrac{-2 - 1}{-4 - (-4)}$

$$= \frac{-3}{0}$$

$\therefore$ gradient of AB is undefined.
AB is a vertical line and its equation is $x = -4$.

Gradient of $BC = \dfrac{5 - (-2)}{2 - (-4)}$

$$= \frac{7}{6}$$

Let the equation of BC be $y = \frac{7}{6}x + k$.

Since $C(2, 5)$ is on the line,

$$5 = \frac{7}{6}(2) + k$$

$$k = \frac{8}{3}$$

$\therefore$ the equation of BC is $y = \frac{7}{6}x + \frac{8}{3}$.

Gradient of $CA = \dfrac{5 - 1}{2 - (-4)}$

$$= \frac{2}{3}$$

Let the equation of CA be $y = \frac{2}{3}x + k$.

Since $C(2, 5)$ is on the line,

$$5 = \frac{2}{3}(2) + k$$

$$k = \frac{11}{3}$$

$\therefore$ the equation of CA is $y = \frac{2}{3}x + \frac{11}{3}$.

(b) y-intercept of $AC = \dfrac{11}{3}$

$\therefore$ the required coordinates are $\left(0, 3\frac{2}{3}\right)$.

(c) $AB = 1 - (-2)$
$$= 3$$
Height from C to $AB = 2 - (-4)$
$$= 6$$
$\therefore$ area of $\triangle ABC = \frac{1}{2} \times 3 \times 6$
$$= 9 \text{ units}^2$$

(d) $BC = \sqrt{(2 + 4)^2 + [5 - (-2)]^2}$
$$= \sqrt{85} \text{ units}$$
Let h units be the perpendicular distance from A to BC.
Consider the area of $\triangle ABC$, we have

$$\frac{1}{2} \times h \times \sqrt{85} = 9$$

$\therefore$ $h = \dfrac{18}{\sqrt{85}}$
$$= 1.95 \text{ units} \quad \text{(correct to 3 sig. fig.)}$$
The perpendicular distance from A to BC is 1.95 units.

11. A hotel will cater for a party at the cost of $30 per person plus a basic charge of $200. Let y be the total cost for x persons.
    (a) Copy and complete the following table.

No. of persons (x)	20	40	60	80	100
Total cost (y)	800	1400	2000	2600	3200

    (b) Write a linear equation in terms of x and y.

(c) Suppose the graph of the linear equation in **(b)** is drawn.
    (i) What is the gradient of the line? What does the gradient represent?
    (ii) What is the y-intercept of the line? What does the y-intercept represent?

Solution
(b) $y = 30x + 200$
(c) **(i)** Gradient of the line = 30
        It represents the additional charge per person.
    (ii) y-intercept of the line = 200
        It represents the basic cost of the party.

12. The vertices of $\triangle OAB$ are the origin O, $A(-15, 0)$ and $B(0, 8)$.
  (a) Find the equation of the line AB.
  (b) Find the equation of the perpendicular bisectors
    (i) L_1, of OA, and   **(ii)** L_2, of OB.
  (c) Suppose G is the intersecting point of L_1 and L_2.
    (i) Find the coordinates of G.
    (ii) Show that G is on the line AB.
  (d) Find the lengths of OG, AG and BG.
  (e) What is the relationship between G and $\triangle OAB$?

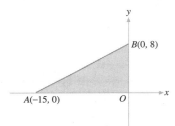

Solution
(a)   Gradient of $AB = \dfrac{8 - 0}{0 - (-15)}$
                    $= \dfrac{8}{15}$
    y-intercept of $AB = 8$
    $\therefore$ the equation of the line AB is $y = \dfrac{8}{15}x + 8$.

(b) **(i)** Midpoint of $OA = \left(-\dfrac{15}{2}, 0\right)$
        The perpendicular bisector L_1 of OA is a vertical line passing through $\left(-\dfrac{15}{2}, 0\right)$.
        $\therefore$ the equation of L_1 is $x = -\dfrac{15}{2}$.

    (ii) Midpoint of $OB = (0, 4)$
        The perpendicular bisector L_2 of OB is a horizontal line passing through $(0, 4)$.
        $\therefore$ the equation of L_2 is $y = 4$.

(c) **(i)** The coordinates of G are $\left(-\dfrac{15}{2}, 4\right)$.

    (ii) Gradient of $AG = \dfrac{4 - 0}{-\dfrac{15}{2} - (-15)}$
                        $= \dfrac{8}{15}$
       $\therefore$ gradient of AG = gradient of AB
       Hence, A, G and B lie on the same straight line.
       i.e. G is on the line AB.

(d) $OG = \sqrt{\left(-\dfrac{15}{2} - 0\right)^2 + (4 - 0)^2} = 8.5$ units

      $AG = \sqrt{\left(-\dfrac{15}{2} + 15\right)^2 + (4 - 0)^2} = 8.5$ units

      $BG = \sqrt{\left(-\dfrac{15}{2} - 0\right)^2 + (4 - 8)^2} = 8.5$ units

(e)   From **(d)**, $OG = AG = BG$.
    $\therefore$ G is the midpoint of the side AB of $\triangle OAB$ and G is the circumcentre of $\triangle OAB$.

Brainworks

13. A line L passes through the point $A(-1, 3)$. It makes an angle of $45°$ with the x-axis. Find the equation of L.

Solution
When a line L makes an angle of $45°$ with the x-axis, the gradient of the line is 1 or -1.
Case 1 Gradient = 1
        Let the equation of L be $y = x + h$.
        Since $A(-1, 3)$ is on L,
        $3 = -1 + h$
        $h = 4$
        $\therefore$ the equation of L is $y = x + 4$.
Case 2 Gradient = -1
        Let the equation of L be $y = -x + k$.
        Since $A(-1, 3)$ is on L,
        $3 = -(-1) + k$
        $k = 2$
        $\therefore$ the equation of L is $y = -x + 2$.

Revision Exercise 9

1. The vertices of $\triangle ABC$ are $A(-1, 2)$, $B(1, 5)$ and $C(4, 3)$.
  (a) Find the lengths of the sides AB, BC and CA.
  (b) What type of triangle is $\triangle ABC$?
  (c) Find the perpendicular distance from B to AC.
  (d) Find the coordinates of the point at which the line AC cuts the x-axis.

Solution

(a) $AB = \sqrt{(1 - (-1)^2 + (5 - 2)^2}$

$= \sqrt{13}$ units

$BC = \sqrt{(4 - 1)^2 + (3 - 5)^2}$

$= \sqrt{13}$ units

$CA = \sqrt{(-1 - 4)^2 + (2 - 3)^2}$

$= \sqrt{26}$ units

(b) Since $AB = BC$,

∴ $\triangle ABC$ is isosceles.

$AB^2 + BC^2 = 13 + 13$

$= 26$

∴ $AB^2 + BC^2 = CA^2$

$\angle ABC = 90°$ (converse of Pythagoras'
Theorem)

Hence, $\triangle ABC$ is a right-angled isosceles triangle.

(c) Let h units be the perpendicular distance from B
to AC.

Considering the area of $\triangle ABC$,

$\frac{1}{2} \times h \times AC = \frac{1}{2} \times AB \times BC$

$h \times \sqrt{26} = \sqrt{13} \times \sqrt{13}$

$h = \frac{13}{\sqrt{26}}$

$= 2.55$ (correct to 3 sig. fig.)

∴ the required distance is 2.55 units.

(d) Let $T(t, 0)$ be the point that AC cuts the x-axis.

Gradient of AT = gradient of AC

$\frac{0 - 2}{t - (-1)} = \frac{3 - 2}{4 - (-1)}$

$\frac{-2}{t + 1} = \frac{1}{5}$

$-10 = t + 1$

$t = -11$

i.e. the required point is $(-11, 0)$.

2. A line L passes through $A(-2, 3)$ and its gradient is $\frac{1}{2}$.

(a) Find the equation of L.

(b) If the point $B(4, k)$ lies on L, find the value of k.

(c) Find the lengths of OA and OB, where O is the
origin.

(d) Find the area of $\triangle OAB$.

(e) Find the value of $\sin \angle AOB$.

Solution

(a) Let the equation of L be

$y = \frac{1}{2}x + c$.

Since $A(-2, 3)$ is on L,

$3 = \frac{1}{2}(-2) + c$

$c = 4$

∴ the equation of L is $y = \frac{1}{2}x + 4$.

(b) If $B(4, k)$ is on L,

$k = \frac{1}{2}(4) + 4$

∴ $k = 6$

(c) $OA = \sqrt{(-2 - 0)^2 + (3 - 0)^2}$

$= \sqrt{13}$ units

$OB = \sqrt{(4 - 0)^2 + (6 - 0)^2}$

$= \sqrt{52}$ units

(d)

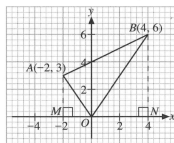

Refer to the above diagram.

Area of trapezium $AMNB = \frac{1}{2} \times (3 + 6) \times 6$

$= 27$ units^2

Area of $\triangle OAM = \frac{1}{2} \times 3 \times 2$

$= 3$ units^2

Area of $\triangle OBN = \frac{1}{2} \times 4 \times 6$

$= 12$ units^2

∴ area of $\triangle OAB = 27 - 3 - 12$

$= 12$ units^2

(e) $\frac{1}{2} \times OA \times OB \times \sin \angle AOB = $ area of $\triangle OAB$

$\frac{1}{2} \times \sqrt{13} \times \sqrt{52} \times \sin \angle AOB = 12$

∴ $\sin \angle AOB = \frac{12}{13}$

3. In the diagram, A is the point $(0, -10)$ and D is the point
$(0, 6)$. CD is a horizontal line. The line AC cuts the x-axis
at B and its gradient is $\frac{5}{2}$.

(a) Find the equation of the line CD.

(b) Find the equation of
the line AC.

(c) Find the coordinates
of B.

(d) Find the coordinates
of C.

(e) Hence find the area of
$\triangle ACD$.

(f) What is the ratio of
areas of $\triangle ABO$ and
$\triangle ACD$?

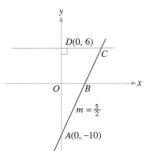

Solution

(a) CD is a horizontal line and D is $(0, 6)$.

∴ the equation of CD is $y = 6$.

(b) Since gradient of $AC = \dfrac{5}{2}$ and y-intercept $= -10$,

the equation of the line AC is $y = \dfrac{5}{2}x - 10$.

(c) Let the coordinates of B be $(b, 0)$.

Since $B(b, 0)$ is on the line AC,

$0 = \dfrac{5}{2}b - 10$

$b = 4$

i.e. the coordinates of B are $(4, 0)$.

(d) Let the coordinates of C be $(k, 6)$.

Since C is on the line AC,

$6 = \dfrac{5}{2}k - 10$

$k = \dfrac{32}{5}$

i.e. the coordinates of C are $\left(\dfrac{32}{5}, 6\right)$.

(e) Area of $\triangle ACD = \dfrac{1}{2} \times AD \times CD$

$= \dfrac{1}{2} \times 16 \times \dfrac{32}{5}$

$= 51.2$ units^2

(f) Area of $\triangle ABO = \dfrac{1}{2} \times OA \times OB$

$= \dfrac{1}{2} \times 10 \times 4$

$= 20$ units^2

Area of $\triangle ABO$: area of $\triangle ACD = 20 : 51.2$

$= 25 : 64$

4. The vertices of a quadrilateral $ABCD$ are $A(-3, 0)$, $B(4, 1)$, $C(5, 4)$ and $D(-2, 3)$. $G(1, 2)$ is a point inside $ABCD$.

(a) Draw a diagram to show $ABCD$.

(b) Find the lengths of AG, BG, CG and DG.

(c) Do the points A, G and C lie on a straight line?

(d) Do the points B, G and D lie on a straight line?

(e) From the results in **(b)**, **(c)** and **(d)**, what can you say about G?

(f) What type of quadrilateral is $ABCD$?

Solution

(a)

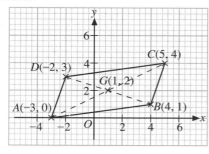

(b) $AG = \sqrt{(1 - (-3))^2 + (2 - 0)^2}$

$= \sqrt{20}$ units

$BG = \sqrt{(1 - 4)^2 + (2 - 1)^2}$

$= \sqrt{10}$ units

$CG = \sqrt{(1 - 5)^2 + (2 - 4)^2}$

$= \sqrt{20}$ units

$DG = \sqrt{(1 - (-2))^2 + (2 - 3)^2}$

$= \sqrt{10}$ units

(c) Gradient of $AC = \dfrac{4 - 0}{5 - (-3)} = \dfrac{1}{2}$

Gradient of $AG = \dfrac{2 - 0}{1 - (-3)} = \dfrac{1}{2}$

∴ gradient of AC = gradient of AG

Hence, A, G and C lie on a straight line.

(d) Gradient of $BD = \dfrac{3 - 1}{-2 - 4} = -\dfrac{1}{3}$

Gradient of $BG = \dfrac{2 - 1}{1 - 4} = -\dfrac{1}{3}$

∴ gradient of BD = gradient of BG

Hence, B, G and D lie on a straight line.

(e) From **(b)** and **(c)**, G is the point of intersection of AC and BD.

From **(d)**, the point G bisects the line segments AC and BD.

(f) $ABCD$ is a parallelogram.

5. In the diagram, the vertices of $\triangle OPQ$ are the origin O, $P(a, b)$ and $Q(c, d)$.

(a) Plot the points $R(2a, 2b)$ and $S(2c, 2d)$ on the diagram.

(b) Determine whether the following sets of points lie on a straight line.

(i) O, P, R **(ii)** O, Q, S

(c) Find the gradients of PQ and RS. Are they equal?

(d) Find the ratio $OP : OR$.

(e) What is the relationship between $\triangle OPQ$ and $\triangle ORS$?

(f) Find the ratio of areas of $\triangle OPQ$ and $\triangle ORS$.

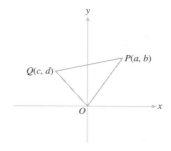

Solution

(a)

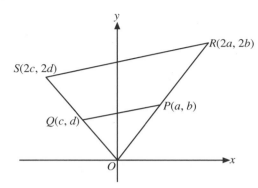

(b) **(i)** Gradient of $OP = \dfrac{b-0}{a-0}$

$= \dfrac{b}{a}$

Gradient of $OR = \dfrac{2b-0}{2a-0}$

$= \dfrac{b}{a}$

$\therefore$ gradient of OP = gradient of OR

Hence, O, P and R lie on a straight line.

(ii) Gradient of $OQ = \dfrac{d-0}{c-0}$

$= \dfrac{d}{c}$

Gradient of $OS = \dfrac{2d-0}{2c-0}$

$= \dfrac{d}{c}$

$\therefore$ gradient of OQ = gradient of OS

Hence, O, Q and S lie on a straight line.

(c) Gradient of $PQ = \dfrac{b-d}{a-c}$

Gradient of $RS = \dfrac{2b-2d}{2a-2c}$

$= \dfrac{2(b-d)}{2(a-c)}$

$= \dfrac{b-d}{a-c}$

$\therefore$ gradients of PQ and RS are equal.

(d) $OP = \sqrt{(a-0)^2 + (b-0)^2}$

$= \sqrt{a^2 + b^2}$ units

$OR = \sqrt{(2a-0)^2 + (2b-0)^2}$

$= \sqrt{4a^2 + 4b^2}$

$= \sqrt{4(a^2 + b^2)}$

$= 2\sqrt{a^2 + b^2}$ units

$\therefore$ $OP : OR = \sqrt{a^2+b^2} : 2\sqrt{a^2+b^2}$

$= 1 : 2$

(e) Similar to the steps in **(d)**, we have

$OQ : OS = 1 : 2$

In $\triangle OPQ$ and $\triangle ORS$,

$\dfrac{OP}{OR} = \dfrac{OQ}{OS}$

$= \dfrac{1}{2}$

$\angle POQ = \angle ROS$ (common)

$\therefore$ $\triangle OPQ$ is similar to $\triangle ORS$.

(Side-Angle-Side similarity)

(f) Area of $\triangle OPQ$: area of $\triangle OSR = OP^2 : OR^2$

$= 1^2 : 2^2$

$= 1 : 4$

6.

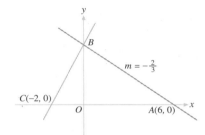

In the diagram, the coordinates of the points A and C are $(6, 0)$ and $(-2, 0)$ respectively. The gradient of the line AB is $-\dfrac{2}{3}$. Find

(a) the equation of the line AB,

(b) the coordinates of B,

(c) the equation of the line BC,

(d) the lengths of AB, BC and CA,

(e) the value of cos $\angle ABC$,

(f) the type of angle of $\angle ABC$.

Solution

(a) Let the equation of the line AB be $y = -\dfrac{2}{3}x + h$.

Since $A(6, 0)$ is on AB, $\quad 0 = -\dfrac{2}{3}(6) + h$

$h = 4$

$\therefore$ the equation of the line AB is $y = -\dfrac{2}{3}x + 4$.

(b) y-intercept of the line $AB = 4$

$\therefore$ the coordinates of B are $(0, 4)$.

(c) Gradient of $BC = \dfrac{4-0}{0-(-2)}$

$= 2$

y-intercept of $BC = 4$

$\therefore$ the equation of the line BC is $y = 2x + 4$.

(d) $AB = \sqrt{(0-6)^2 + (4-0)^2}$

$= \sqrt{52}$ units

$BC = \sqrt{(-2-0)^2 + (0-4)^2}$

$= \sqrt{20}$ units

$CA = [6 - (-2)]$

$= 8$ units

(e) By the cosine rule,

$$\cos \angle ABC = \frac{a^2 + c^2 - b^2}{2ac}$$

$$= \frac{20 + 52 - 8^2}{2(\sqrt{20})(\sqrt{52})}$$

$$= 0.124 \quad \text{(correct to 3 sig. fig.)}$$

(f) Since $\cos \angle ABC > 0$, $\angle ABC$ is an acute angle.
(**Note:** $\angle ABC = 82.9°$)

7.

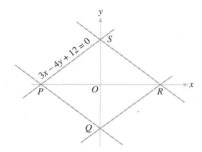

In the diagram, $PQRS$ is a rhombus and the equation of PS is $3x - 4y + 12 = 0$.
(a) Express the equation of the line PS in the gradient-intercept form.
(b) Write down the gradient of PS.
(c) Find the coordinates of P, Q, R and S.
(d) Find the gradient of RS.
(e) Write down the equations of PQ, QR and RS in the gradient-intercept form.

Solution
(a) $PS : 3x - 4y + 12 = 0$
$$4y = 3x + 12$$
$$y = \frac{3}{4}x + 3$$
is the gradient-intercept form of PS.

(b) Gradient of $PS = \frac{3}{4}$

(c) y-intercept of $PS = 3$
∴ the coordinates of S are $(0, 3)$.
Let $(p, 0)$ be the coordinates of P.
Since P is on the line PS,
$$3p - 4(0) + 12 = 0$$
$$p = -4$$
∴ the coordinates of P are $(-4, 0)$.
By the symmetry of the rhombus, the coordinates of R are $(4, 0)$, and the coordinates of Q are $(0, -3)$.

(d) Gradient of $RS = \frac{3 - 0}{0 - 4}$
$$= -\frac{3}{4}$$

(e) Gradient of $PQ = \frac{-3 - 0}{0 - (-4)}$
$$= \frac{3}{4}$$
Gradient of $QR = \frac{0 - (-3)}{4 - 0}$
$$= \frac{3}{4}$$
∴ the equation of line PQ is $y = -\frac{3}{4}x - 3$.
The equation of line QR is $y = \frac{3}{4}x - 3$.
The equation of line RS is $y = -\frac{3}{4}x + 3$.

8. In the diagram, the vertex A of $\triangle ABC$ is $(6\sqrt{3}, 0)$, the gradient of AB is $-\frac{1}{\sqrt{3}}$ and $AB = AC$.
(a) Find the equation of the line AB.
(b) Find the coordinates of B.
(c) Find the coordinates of C.
(d) Find the equation of the line AC.
(e) Find the lengths of AB and BC.
(f) What type of triangle is $\triangle ABC$?

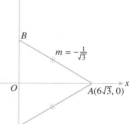

Solution
(a) Let the equation of AB be $y = -\frac{1}{\sqrt{3}}x + b$.
Since $A(6\sqrt{3}, 0)$ is on the line,
$$0 = -\frac{1}{\sqrt{3}}(6\sqrt{3}) + b$$
$$b = 6$$
∴ the equation of AB is $y = -\frac{1}{\sqrt{3}}x + 6$.

(b) y-intercept of $AB = 6$
∴ the coordinates of B are $(0, 6)$.

(c) By symmetry,
the coordinates of C are $(0, -6)$.

(d) Gradient of $AC = \frac{-6 - 0}{0 - 6\sqrt{3}}$
$$= \frac{1}{\sqrt{3}}$$
∴ the equation of AC is $y = \frac{1}{\sqrt{3}}x - 6$.

(e) $AB = \sqrt{(0 - 6\sqrt{3})^2 + (6 - 0)^2}$
$$= 12 \text{ units}$$
$BC = [6 - (-6)]$
$$= 12 \text{ units}$$

(f) As $AB = AC = BC$, $\triangle ABC$ is an equilateral triangle.

9. In the diagram, $OABC$ is a square and the vertex A is $(a, 0)$. Points P, Q, R and S are marked on the sides of the square such that $OP = AQ = BR = CS = 1$ unit.
   (a) State the coordinates of the points B, C, P, Q, R and S.
   (b) Find the lengths of PQ and QR.
   (c) Is $\triangle APQ$ congruent to $\triangle BQR$? Why?
   (d) Show that $\angle PQR$ is a right angle.
   (e) What type of quadrilateral is $PQRS$?
   (f) Find the equation of the line RS.

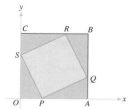

Solution
(a) The coordinates of B are (a, a).
   The coordinates of C are $(0, a)$.
   The coordinates of P are $(1, 0)$.
   The coordinates of Q are $(a, 1)$.
   The coordinates of R are $(a - 1, a)$.
   The coordinates of S are $(0, a - 1)$.

(b) $PQ = \sqrt{(a-1)^2 + (1-0)^2}$
   $= \sqrt{a^2 - 2a + 2}$ units
   $QR = \sqrt{(a-1-a)^2 + (a-1)^2}$
   $= \sqrt{a^2 - 2a + 2}$ units

(c) In $\triangle APQ$ and $\triangle BQR$,
   $PQ = QR$ (proven)
   $AQ = BR$
       $= 1$ (given)
   $AP = BQ$
       $= a - 1$ (proven)
   $\therefore \triangle APQ \equiv \triangle BQR$ (SSS)

(d) $\angle APQ = \angle BQR$ (corr. parts of $\equiv \triangle$s)
       $\angle PQB = \angle APQ + \angle PAQ$ (ext. $\angle$ of $\triangle$)
   $\angle PQR + \angle BQR = \angle BQR + 90°$
   $\therefore$ $\angle PQR = 90°$

(e) Similar to the steps in (d), we can show that the sides of $PQRS$ are equal and all its angles are right angles.
   $\therefore PQRS$ is a square.

(f) Gradient of $RS = \dfrac{a-1-a}{0-(a-1)} = \dfrac{1}{a-1}$
   $\therefore$ the equation of RS is $y = \dfrac{1}{a-1}x + (a-1)$,
   i.e. $y = \dfrac{1}{a-1}x + a - 1$.

10. The diagram shows a quadratic graph $y = -x^2 + x + 6$ which cuts the x-axis at A and B, and the y-axis at C. Find
   (a) the coordinates of A, B and C,
   (b) the length of AC,
   (c) the equation of BC,
   (d) the ratio of the areas of $\triangle OAC$ and $\triangle OBC$.

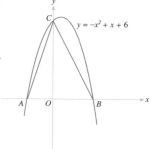

Solution
(a) $y = -x^2 + x + 6$ .... (1)
   Putting $x = 0$ into (1),
       $y = -6^2 + 0 + 6$
       $= 6$
   $\therefore$ the coordinates of C are $(0, 6)$.
   Putting $y = 0$ into (1),
       $0 = -x^2 + x + 6$
       $x^2 - x - 6 = 0$
       $(x + 2)(x - 3) = 0$
       $x = -2$ or $x = 3$
   $\therefore$ the coordinates of A are $(-2, 0)$.
   the coordinates of B are $(3, 0)$.

(b) $AC = \sqrt{[0-(-2)]^2 + (6-0)^2}$
       $= \sqrt{40}$ units

(c) Gradient of $BC = \dfrac{6-0}{0-3} = -2$
   $\therefore$ the equation of BC is $y = -2x + 6$.

(d) Area of $\triangle OAC$: area of $\triangle OBC$
   $= \dfrac{1}{2} \times 2 \times 6 : \dfrac{1}{2} \times 3 \times 6$
   $= 2 : 3$

Chapter 10   Arc Lengths And Sector Areas

Class Activity 1

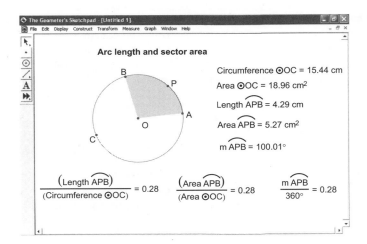

Let us investigate the relationship between arc length, angle subtended by arc and circumference using Sketchpad.

Tasks

(a) Construct a circle with centre O and a point C on the circle.

(b) Mark three points A, P and B on the circle in order.

(c) Click the above three points in order. Select **Construct | Arc Through 3 Points** to construct the arc APB.

(d) Click the arc and then select **Measure | Arc Length** to measure the length of the arc APB.

(e) Click the circle and then select **Measure | Circumference** to measure the circumference of the circle.

(f) Click the arc and then select **Measure | Arc Angle** to measure angle AOB.

(g) Calculate the ratio of arc length APB to the circumference of the circle.

(h) Calculate the ratio of arc angle AOB to $360°$.

(i) Drag the point B around and observe the changes in the measurements and ratios.

Question

1. Suggest a relationship between the two ratios obtained in tasks **(g)** and **(h)**.

$$\frac{\text{arc length } APB}{\text{circumference}} = \frac{\text{arc angle } AOB}{360°}$$

Class Activity 2

Let us now investigate the relationship between sector area, angle subtended by arc and the area of the circle. Refer to the diagram in Class Activity 1.

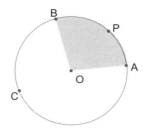

Tasks

(a) Construct a circle with centre O and a point C on the circle.

(b) Mark three points A, P, and B on the circle in order.

(c) Construct the arc APB.

(d) Click the arc and select **Construct | Arc Sector** to construct the sector $OAPB$.

(e) Click the sector and select **Measure | Area**.

(f) Click the circle and select **Measure | Area**.

(g) Calculate the ratio of the area of sector $OAPB$ to the area of circle.

(h) Calculate the ratio of the angle AOB at the centre to 360°.

(i) Drag the point B and observe the changes in both ratios obtained in tasks **(g)** and **(h)**.

Question

1. Suggest a relationship between the two ratios obtained in tasks **(g)** and **(h)**.

$$\frac{\text{area of sector } OAPB}{\text{area of circle}} = \frac{\text{angle } AOB}{360°}$$

Extend Your Learning Curve

Traffic Roundabout

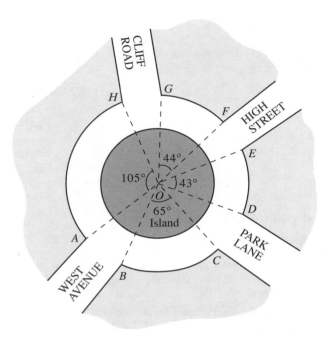

The diagram shows a roundabout at the junction of four roads. The central island is in the form of a circle with centre O and diameter 30 m. The curbs BC, DE, FG and HA are in the form of arcs that lie on a circle with centre O and diameter 66 m. The angles subtended by these curbs at O are 65°, 43°, 44° and 105° respectively.

(a) Find the total length of the curbs.

(b) Find the area of the circular road surrounding the island.

(c) Do you know the reason why traffic roundabouts are built? Do some research and find out.

Solution

(a) Total length of the curbs $= \dfrac{65° + 43° + 44° + 105°}{360°} \times 2\pi \times 33$

$\qquad\qquad\qquad\qquad\quad = \dfrac{257}{360} \times 2\pi \times 33$

$\qquad\qquad\qquad\qquad\quad = 148$ m   (correct to 3 sig. fig.)

(b) Area of the circular asphalt road $= \pi \times 33^2 - \pi \times 15^2$

$\qquad\qquad\qquad\qquad\qquad\qquad\quad = 2710$ m^2 (correct to 3 sig. fig.)

(c) The purposes of building a traffic roundabout are:

1. increase the throughput of traffic at a junction;

2. improve vehicle and pedestrian safety.

More information can be found at:
http://en.wikipedia.org/wiki/Roundabout_intersection

Try It!

Section 10.1

1. The radius of a circle is 8 cm. If an arc CQD subtends an angle of 135° at the centre, find its length.

Solution

Length of arc $CQD = \dfrac{135°}{360°} \times 2\pi \times 8$

$\qquad\qquad\qquad\quad = 18.8$ cm (correct to 3 sig. fig.)

2. The minute hand of a clock is 10 cm long.
   (a) How far does the tip of the minute hand travel in 40 minutes?
   (b) How long will it take the tip to move 30 cm?

Solution

(a) Angle of rotation in 40 min $= \dfrac{40}{60} \times 360°$

$\qquad\qquad\qquad\qquad\qquad = 240°$

∴ distance travelled by the tip

$= \dfrac{240°}{360°} \times 2\pi \times 10$

$= 41.9$ cm (correct to 3 sig. fig.)

(b) Let $x°$ be the angle of rotation of the minute hand when the tip moves 30 cm.

$\dfrac{x}{360} \times 2\pi \times 10 = 30$

$\qquad\qquad x = \dfrac{30 \times 360}{2\pi \times 10}$

$\qquad\qquad\quad = 171.89$

∴ the required time $= \dfrac{171.89}{360} \times 60$

$\qquad\qquad\qquad\quad = 28.6$ minutes

$\qquad\qquad\qquad\qquad$ (correct to 3 sig. fig.)

3. A piece of wire is 80 cm long. It is bent into a sector of a circle which subtends an angle of 130° at the centre of the circle. Find the radius of the circle.

Solution

Let r cm be the radius of the circle.

$r + r + \dfrac{130}{360} \times 2\pi \times r = 80$

$\qquad \left(2 + \dfrac{13\pi}{18}\right) r = 80$

$\qquad\qquad\qquad r = \dfrac{80}{2 + \dfrac{13\pi}{8}}$

$\qquad\qquad\qquad\quad = 18.7$ (correct to 3 sig. fig.)

∴ the radius of the circle is 18.7 cm.

Section 10.2

4. In the diagram, $OCQD$ is a sector of the circle with centre O and radius 9 cm. Given that reflex $\angle COD = 237°$, find the area of the sector $OCQD$.

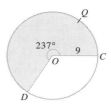

Solution

Area of sector $OCQD = \dfrac{237}{360} \times \pi \times 9^2$

$\qquad\qquad\qquad\qquad\quad = 168$ cm^2 (correct to 3 sig. fig.)

5. In the diagram, $OAPB$ is a sector of a circle with centre O and radius 8 cm. The area of the sector is 64 cm^2. Find
   (a) $\angle AOB$,
   (b) the area of the segment APB.

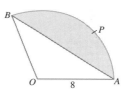

Solution

(a) Let $\angle AOB = x°$

$\dfrac{x}{360} \times \pi \times 8^2 = 64$

$\qquad\qquad x = \dfrac{360}{\pi}$

$\qquad\qquad\quad = 114.59$

∴ $\angle AOB = 115°$ (correct to 3 sig. fig.)

(b) Area of $\triangle OAB = \dfrac{1}{2} \times 8 \times 8 \times \sin 114.59°$

$\qquad\qquad\qquad\qquad = 29.098$ cm^2

Area of the segment ABP

$= 64 - 29.098$

$= 34.9$ cm^2 (correct to 3 sig. fig.)

6. In the diagram, OQR and OPS are sectors of two circles with a common centre O. $OP = 5$ cm, $PQ = x$ cm and $\angle POS = 144°$. If the area of the shaded part is 30π cm^2, find the value of x.

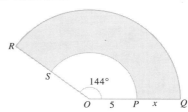

Solution

Area of shaded part = 30π cm^2

$$\frac{144}{360} \times \pi \times (5 + x)^2 - \frac{144}{360} \times \pi \times 5^2 = 30\,\pi$$

$$\frac{2}{5}(5 + x)^2 - 10 = 30$$

$$\frac{2}{5}(5 + x)^2 = 40$$

$$(5 + x)^2 = 100$$

$$5 + x = \sqrt{100} \quad \text{or} \quad -\sqrt{100}$$
$$\text{(rejected)}$$

$$5 + x = 10$$

$$\therefore \quad x = 5$$

Section 10.3

7. Express the following angles in radians.
   (a) 45°
   (b) 200°

Solution

(a) $45° = 45 \times \dfrac{\pi}{180}$ rad.

   $= \dfrac{\pi}{4}$ rad.

   $= 0.785$ rad.   (correct to 3 sig. fig.)

(b) $200° = 200 \times \dfrac{\pi}{180}$ rad.

   $= 3.49$ rad.   (correct to 3 sig. fig.)

8. Express the following angles in degrees.
   (a) $\dfrac{7\pi}{4}$ rad.   (b) 4.7 rad.

Solution

(a) $\dfrac{7\pi}{4}$ rad. $= \dfrac{7\pi}{4} \times \dfrac{180°}{\pi}$

   $= 315°$

(b) 4.7 rad. $= 4.7 \times \dfrac{180°}{\pi}$

   $= 269°$ (correct to 3 sig. fig.)

9. Find the values of the following.
   (a) $\tan \dfrac{\pi}{4}$

   (b) $\sin (1.3$ rad.$)$

Solution

(a) $\tan \dfrac{\pi}{4} = 1$

(b) $\sin (1.3$ rad.$) = 0.964$ (correct to 3 sig. fig.)

Section 10.4

10. In the diagram, OAB is a sector of a circle with centre O. $OA = 5$ cm and $\angle AOB = 2.4$ rad. Find
    (a) the length of the arc AB,
    (b) the area of the sector OAB.

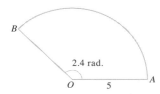

Solution

(a) Length of arc $AB = 5 \times 2.4$

   $= 12$ cm

(b) Area of sector $OAB = \dfrac{1}{2} \times 5^2 \times 2.4$

   $= 30$ cm^2

11. The area of a sector of a circle is 75 cm^2. If the arc length of the sector is 15 cm, find
    (a) the radius of the circle,
    (b) the angle subtended at the centre by the arc.

Solution

(a) Let r cm be the radius of the circle.

   $\dfrac{1}{2} \times r \times 15 = 75$

   $r = 10$

   The radius of the circle is 10 cm.

(b) Let θ rad. be the angle subtended at the centre by the arc.

   $r\theta = 15$

   $10\theta = 15$

   $\theta = 1.5$

   The angle subtended at the centre is 1.5 rad.

12. In the diagram, PT and QT are tangents to the circle, centre O, at P and Q respectively. The shaded region is enclosed by the tangents PT and QT, and the minor arc PQ. $OP = 8$ cm and $OT = 16$ cm. Find
    (a) $\angle POQ$ in radians,
    (b) the perimeter of the shaded region,
    (c) the area of the shaded region.

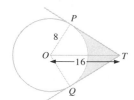

Solution

(a) $\quad \angle OPT = 90°$ $\qquad$ (tangent $\perp$ radius)

$\quad \cos \angle POT = \dfrac{8}{16}$

$\qquad \angle POT = \dfrac{\pi}{3}$ rad.

$\qquad\qquad = 1.0472$ rad.

$\quad \angle POQ = 2 \times \angle POT$

$\qquad\qquad = \dfrac{2\pi}{3}$ rad.

$\qquad\qquad = 2.0944$ rad.

$\qquad\qquad = 2.09$ rad. $\quad$ (correct to 3 sig. fig.)

(b) $\qquad PT^2 = 16^2 - 8^2$

$\qquad\quad PT = \sqrt{192}$ cm

Length of minor arc $PQ = 8 \times \dfrac{2\pi}{3}$

$\qquad\qquad\qquad\qquad\quad = \dfrac{16\pi}{3}$ cm

$\therefore$ perimeter of the shaded region

$\quad = 2 \times \sqrt{192} + \dfrac{16\pi}{3}$

$\quad = 44.5$ cm $\quad$ (correct to 3 sig. fig.)

(c) $\quad$ Area of quadrilateral $OPTQ$

$\quad = 2 \times$ area of $\triangle OPT$

$\quad = 2 \times \dfrac{1}{2} \times 8 \times \sqrt{192}$

$\quad = 8\sqrt{192}$ cm^2

Area of minor sector $OPQ = \dfrac{1}{2} \times 8^2 \times \dfrac{2\pi}{3}$

$\qquad\qquad\qquad\qquad\qquad = \dfrac{64\pi}{3}$ cm^2

$\therefore$ area of the shaded region

$\quad = 8\sqrt{192} - \dfrac{64\pi}{3}$

$\quad = 43.8$ cm^2 $\quad$ (correct to 3 sig. fig.)

Exercise 10.1

The unit of length in the diagrams is cm, unless otherwise stated.

Basic Practice

1. Find the length of arc *APB* in each of the following.

   (a)

   (b)

   (c)

   (d)

   Solution

   (a) Length of arc *APB*

   $= \dfrac{80°}{360°} \times 2\pi \times 9$

   $= 12.6$ cm   (correct to 3 sig. fig.)

   (b) Length of arc *APB*

   $= \dfrac{240°}{360°} \times 2\pi \times 5$

   $= 20.9$ cm   (correct to 3 sig. fig.)

   (c) Length of arc *APB*

   $= \dfrac{130°}{360°} \times 2\pi \times 16$

   $= 36.3$ cm   (correct to 3 sig. fig.)

   (d) Reflex $\angle AOB = 360° - 55°$ ($\angle$s at a point)

   $\qquad\qquad\qquad = 305°$

   Length of arc *APB*

   $= \dfrac{305°}{360°} \times 2\pi \times 7$

   $= 37.3$ cm   (correct to 3 sig. fig.)

2. Copy and complete the following table for the arcs of a circle.

	Radius	Subtended Angle	Arc Length
(a)		120°	25 cm
(b)		230°	6 m
(c)	20 cm		40 cm
(d)	3 m		10 m

Solution

(a) $\dfrac{120}{360} \times 2\pi \times r = 25$

$\qquad r = \dfrac{25 \times 3}{2\pi}$

$\qquad\quad = 11.9$ (correct to 3 sig. fig.)

$\therefore$ radius $= 11.9$ cm

(b) $\dfrac{230}{360} \times 2\pi \times r = 6$

$\qquad r = \dfrac{6 \times 36}{2\pi \times 23}$

$\qquad\quad = 1.49$ (correct to 3 sig. fig.)

$\therefore$ radius $= 1.49$ m

(c) $\dfrac{x}{360} \times 2\pi \times 20 = 40$

$\qquad x = \dfrac{40 \times 360}{40\pi}$

$\qquad\quad = 114.6°$ (correct to 1 d.p.)

$\therefore$ the subtended angle $= 114.6°$

(d) $\dfrac{x}{360} \times 2\pi \times 3 = 10$

$\qquad x = \dfrac{10 \times 360}{6\pi}$

$\qquad\quad = 191.0°$ (correct to 1 d.p.)

$\therefore$ the subtended angle $= 191.0°$

Further Practice

3. The diagram shows a quadrant of a circle of radius 6 cm. Find the perimeter of the quadrant.

   Solution

   Length of arc $AB = \dfrac{90}{360} \times 2\pi \times 6 \times \dfrac{90}{360}$

   $\qquad\qquad\qquad = 3\pi$ cm

   $\therefore$ perimeter of the quadrant

   $\quad = 6 + 6 + 3\pi$

   $\quad = 21.4$ cm   (correct to 3 sig. fig.)

4. In the diagram, *O* is the centre of the circle. *OB* = 8 cm and $\angle APB = 50°$. Find

   (a) $\angle AOB$,

   (b) the length of the arc *AQB*,

   (c) the length of the arc *APB*.

   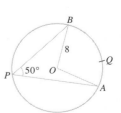

Solution

(a) ∠AOB
= 2∠APB   (∠ at centre = 2∠ at circumference)
= 2 × 50°
= 100°

(b) Length of arc AQB
= $\frac{100}{360}$ × 2π × 8
= 14.0 cm   (correct to 3 sig. fig.)

(c) Reflex ∠AOB = 360° − 100°   (∠s at a point)
= 260°
Length of arc APB
= $\frac{260}{360}$ × 2π × 8
= 36.3 cm   (correct to 3 sig. fig.)

5. The diagram shows a sector OAPB of a circle. OB = 15 cm and AB = 20 cm. Find
(a) ∠AOB,
(b) the length of the arc APB.

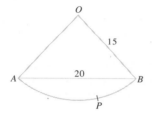

Solution

(a) Draw a perpendicular ON from O to AB.

Then   BN = $\frac{1}{2}$ × 20
= 10 cm

sin ∠BON = $\frac{BN}{OB}$
= $\frac{10}{15}$
∠BON = 41.81°
∴   ∠AOB = 2∠BON
= 83.62°
= 83.6°   (correct to 1 d.p.)

(b) Length of arc APB
= $\frac{83.62}{360}$ × 2π × 15
= 21.9 cm   (correct to 3 sig. fig.)

6. The diagram shows a sector OPQ of a circle. OP = 10 cm and the arc PQ = 21 cm. Find
(a) ∠POQ,
(b) the length of the chord PQ.

Solution

(a) Let ∠POQ = x°.

$\frac{x}{360}$ × 2π × 10 = 21
x = $\frac{21 × 360}{20π}$
= 120.32
= 120.3   (correct to 1 d.p.)
∴   ∠POQ = 120.3°

(b) Drop a perpendicular ON from O to PQ.

∠PON = $\frac{1}{2}$ × 120.32°
= 60.16°
sin ∠PON = $\frac{PN}{OP}$
sin 60.16° = $\frac{PN}{10}$
PN = 8.6742 cm
Length of chord PQ
= 2PN
= 17.3 cm   (correct to 3 sig. fig.)

7. In the diagram, O is the centre of the circle, reflex ∠AOB = 315° and the arc ACB = 24 cm. Find
(a) the radius of the circle,
(b) the length of the minor arc AB.

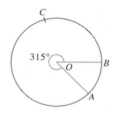

Solution

(a) Let r cm be the radius of the circle.

$\frac{315}{360}$ × 2π × r = 24
r = $\frac{24 × 360}{315 × 2π}$
= 4.365
= 4.37   (correct to 3 sig. fig.)
∴ the radius is 4.37 cm.

(b) ∠AOB = 360° − 315°   (∠s at a point)
= 45°
Length of minor arc AB
= $\frac{45}{360}$ × 2π × 4.365
= 3.43 cm   (correct to 3 sig. fig.)

8. A piece of wire is 90 cm long. It is bent into a sector $OAPB$ of a circle and its arc subtends an angle of 110° at the centre. Find the radius of the circle.

Solution

Let r cm be the radius of the circle.

$$r + r + \frac{110}{360} \times 2\pi \times r = 90$$

$$\left(2 + \frac{11}{18}\pi\right)r = 90$$

$$r = \frac{90}{2 + \frac{11}{18}\pi}$$

$$= 23.0 \text{ (correct to 3 sig. fig.)}$$

The radius of the circle is 23.0 cm.

Maths@Work

9. The end of a 50-cm pendulum describes an arc of 36 cm as it moves from A to B. Through what angle does the pendulum swing?

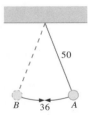

Solution

Let $x°$ be the angle of swing.

$$\frac{x}{360} \times 2\pi \times 50 = 36$$

$$x = \frac{36 \times 360}{100\pi}$$

$$= 41.3 \quad \text{(correct to 3 sig. fig.)}$$

The angle of swing is 41.3°.

10. The wheel of a car is 60 cm in diameter. Find the angle of rotation of the wheel when the car moves forwards by a horizontal distance of 100 cm.

Solution

Let $x°$ be the angle of rotation of the wheel.

$$\frac{x}{360} \times 2\pi \times 30 = 100$$

$$x = \frac{100 \times 360}{60\pi}$$

$$= 191.0 \quad \text{(correct to 1 d.p.)}$$

∴ the angle of rotation is 191.0°.

11. The minute hand of a clock is 12 cm long.
    (a) How far does the tip of the minute hand travel in 25 minutes?
    (b) How long will it take the tip to move 24 cm?

Solution

(a) Angle of rotation of the minute hand

$$= \frac{25}{60} \times 360°$$

$$= 150°$$

∴ distance travelled by the tip

$$= \frac{150}{360} \times 2\pi \times 12$$

$$= 31.4 \text{ cm} \quad \text{(correct to 3 sig. fig.)}$$

(b) Let $x°$ be the angle of rotation when the tip moves 24 cm.

$$\frac{x}{360} \times 2\pi \times 12 = 24$$

$$x = \frac{360}{\pi}$$

$$= 114.59°$$

The required time taken

$$= \frac{114.59}{360} \times 60$$

$$= 19.1 \text{ min} \quad \text{(correct to 3 sig. fig.)}$$

12. Quito (the capital of Ecuador) and Singapore lie very close to the equator. The latitudes and longitudes of Quito and Singapore are 0.2°S 78.5°W and 1.3°N 103.9°E respectively. **Assume** that the radius of the Earth is 6400 km and both cities **lie on the equator**. Find the shortest distance between these two cities.

Solution

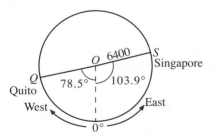

The above diagram shows a top view of the equator, where O is the centre of the Earth.

$\angle QOS = 360° - 78.5° - 103.9°$ ($\angle$s at a point)

$$= 177.6°$$

Shortest distance between the two cities
= length of minor arc QS

$$= \frac{177.6}{360} \times 2\pi \times 6400$$

$$= 19\,838$$

$$= 19\,800 \text{ km} \quad \text{(correct to 3 sig. fig.)}$$

Brainworks

13. The length of an arc of a circle is 3π cm long. Find two possible solutions for the radius of the circle and the angle subtended at the centre by the arc.

Solution

Let r cm be the radius and $x°$ be the angle subtended at the centre.

$$\frac{x}{360} \times 2\pi \times r = 3\pi$$

$$xr = 540$$

When $r = 4$,

$$x = \frac{540}{4}$$

$$= 135$$

When $r = 9$,

$$x = \frac{540}{9}$$

$$= 60$$

∴ two possible sets of solutions are: radius = 4 cm, angle = 135°; and radius = 9 cm, angle = 60°.

Exercise 10.2

In this exercise, the unit of length in each diagram is cm.

Basic Practice

1. Find the area of the sector $OAPB$ in each of the following diagrams.

(a)

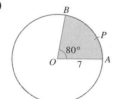

(b)

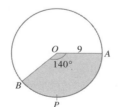

(c)

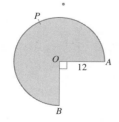

(d)

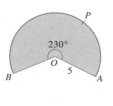

Solution

(a) Area of sector $OAPB$

$$= \frac{80}{360} \times \pi \times 7^2$$

$$= 34.2 \text{ cm}^2 \quad \text{(correct to 3 sig. fig.)}$$

(b) Area of sector $OAPB$

$$= \frac{140}{360} \times \pi \times 9^2$$

$$= 99.0 \text{ cm}^2 \quad \text{(correct to 3 sig. fig.)}$$

(c) Area of sector $OAPB$

$$= \frac{270}{360} \times \pi \times 12^2$$

$$= 339 \text{ cm}^2 \quad \text{(correct to 3 sig. fig.)}$$

(d) Area of sector $OAPB$

$$= \frac{230}{360} \times \pi \times 5^2$$

$$= 50.2 \text{ cm}^2 \quad \text{(correct to 3 sig. fig.)}$$

2. Copy and complete the following table for the sectors of circles.

	Radius	Subtended Angle	Area of Sector
(a)	6 cm	79.6°	25 cm^2
(b)	2 m	143.2°	5 m^2
(c)	7.94 cm	60°	33 cm^2
(d)	2.14 m	150°	6 m^2

Solution

(a) Let $x°$ be the angle subtended at the centre.

$$\frac{x}{360} \times \pi \times 6^2 = 25$$

$$x = \frac{25 \times 360}{36\pi}$$

$$= 79.6 \quad \text{(correct to 1 d.p.)}$$

∴ the subtended angle is 79.6°.

(b) Let $x°$ be the subtended angle.

$$\frac{x}{360} \times \pi \times 2^2 = 5$$

$$x = \frac{5 \times 360}{4\pi}$$

$$= 143.2 \quad \text{(correct to 1 d.p.)}$$

∴ the subtended angle is 143.2°.

(c) Let r cm be the radius.

$$\frac{60}{360} \times \pi \times r^2 = 33$$

$$r = \sqrt{\frac{33 \times 6}{\pi}}$$

$$= 7.94 \quad \text{(correct to 3 sig. fig.)}$$

∴ the radius is 7.94 cm.

(d) Let r cm be the radius.

$$\frac{150}{360} \times \pi \times r^2 = 6$$

$$r = \sqrt{\frac{6 \times 360}{150\pi}}$$

$$= 2.14 \quad \text{(correct to 3 sig. fig.)}$$

∴ the radius is 2.14 m.

Further Practice

3. In the diagram, $ABCD$ is a square of side 3 cm. AC is an arc of the circle with centre B. Find the shaded area.

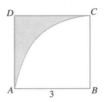

Solution

Area of the square $ABCD = 3^2$

$$= 9 \text{ cm}^2$$

Area of sector $BAC = \frac{90}{360} \times \pi \times 3^2$

$$= \frac{9\pi}{4} \text{ cm}^2$$

Shaded area $= 9 - \frac{9\pi}{4}$

$$= 1.93 \text{ cm}^2 \quad \text{(correct to 3 sig. fig.)}$$

4. In the diagram, $\triangle ABC$ is an equilateral triangle of side 5 cm. Find

(a) the perimeter of the segment BDC,

(b) the area of the segment BDC.

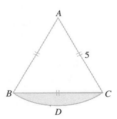

Solution

(a) Length of arc $BDC = \frac{60}{360} \times 2\pi \times 5$

$$= \frac{5\pi}{3} \text{ cm}$$

Perimeter of the segment BDC

$$= 5 + \frac{5\pi}{3}$$

$$= 10.2 \text{ cm} \quad \text{(correct to 3 sig. fig.)}$$

(b) Area of sector $ABDC = \frac{60}{360} \times \pi \times 5^2$

$$= \frac{25\pi}{6} \text{ cm}^2$$

Area of $\triangle ABC = \frac{1}{2} \times 5 \times 5 \times \sin 60°$

$$= \frac{25}{2} \sin 60° \text{ cm}^2$$

∴ area of the segment BDC

$$= \frac{25\pi}{6} - \frac{25}{2} \sin 60°$$

$$= 2.26 \text{ cm}^2 \quad \text{(correct to 3 sig. fig.)}$$

5. In the figure, O is the centre of the circle, $\angle AOB = 45°$ and the area of the sector $OAPB$ is 30 cm². Find

(a) the area of the sector $OAQB$,

(b) the radius of the circle.

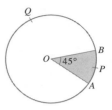

Solution

(a) Reflex $\angle AOB = 360° - 45° \quad (\angle\text{s at a point})$

$$= 315°$$

$$\frac{\text{Area of sector } OAQB}{\text{Area of sector } OAPB} = \frac{\text{reflex } \angle AOB}{\angle AOB}$$

∴ area of sector $OAQB = \frac{315}{45} \times 30 = 210 \text{ cm}^2$

(b) Let r cm be the radius of the circle.

$$\frac{45}{360} \times \pi \times r^2 = 30$$

$$r = \sqrt{\frac{30 \times 360}{45\pi}}$$

$$= 8.74 \quad \text{(correct to 3 sig. fig.)}$$

∴ the radius of the circle is 8.74 cm.

6. In the figure, O is the centre of the circle of radius 6 cm. The area of the sector $OAPB$ is 35 cm². Find

(a) $\angle AOB$,

(b) the area of the segment APB.

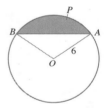

Solution

(a) Let $\angle AOB = x°$

$$\frac{x}{360} \times \pi \times 6^2 = 35$$

$$x = \frac{35 \times 10}{\pi}$$

$$= 111.4 \quad \text{(correct to 1 d.p.)}$$

i.e. $\angle AOB = 111.4°$

(b) Area of $\triangle AOB = \frac{1}{2} \times 6 \times 6 \times \sin 111.4°$

$$= 16.7590 \text{ cm}^2$$

Area of segment ABP

$$= 35 - 16.7590$$

$$= 18.2 \text{ cm}^2 \quad \text{(correct to 3 sig. fig.)}$$

7. In the diagram, AB is a diameter of the circle with centre O, $OB = 8$ cm and $\angle BAC = 35°$. Find

(a) the perimeter of the shaded region $ABPC$,

(b) the area of the shaded region $ABPC$.

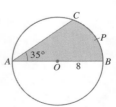

Solution

(a) Draw the segments OC and BC.

$\angle ACB = 90°$ ($\angle$ in a semicircle)

$\dfrac{AC}{AB} = \cos 35°$

$AC = 16 \cos 35°$

$\quad = 13.1064$ cm

$\angle BOC$

$= 2\angle BAC$ ($\angle$ at centre $= 2\angle$ at circumference)

$= 2 \times 35°$

$= 70°$

Length of arc $BPC = \dfrac{70}{360} \times 2\pi \times 8$

$\qquad = 9.7738$ cm

$\therefore$ perimeter of $ABPC$

$= 16 + 9.7738 + 13.1064$

$= 38.9$ cm (correct to 3 sig. fig.)

(b) Area of $\triangle OAC = \dfrac{1}{2} \times 8 \times 8 \times \sin(180° - 70°)$

$\qquad = 30.070$ cm^2

Area of sector $OBPC = \dfrac{70}{360} \times \pi \times 8^2$

$\qquad = 39.095$ cm^2

$\therefore$ area of the shaded region $ABPC$

$= 30.070 + 39.095$

$= 69.2$ cm^2 (correct to 3 sig. fig.)

Maths@Work

8. The diagram shows a fan in which OAD and OBC are sectors of two different circles with centre O. $OA = 9$ cm, $AB = 18$ cm and $\angle AOD = 140°$. Find
   (a) the perimeter of the shaded region,
   (b) the area of the shaded region.

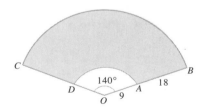

Solution

(a) $OB = 9 + 18$

$\quad = 27$ cm

Length of arc $BC = \dfrac{140}{360} \times 2\pi \times 27$

$\qquad = 65.973$ cm

Length of arc $AD = \dfrac{140}{360} \times 2\pi \times 9$

$\qquad = 21.991$ cm

$\therefore$ perimeter of the shaded region

$= 65.973 + 21.991 + 18 + 18$

$= 124$ cm^2 (correct to 3 sig. fig.)

(b) Area of the shaded region

$= \left(\dfrac{140}{360} \times \pi \times 27^2\right) - \left(\dfrac{140}{360} \times \pi \times 9^2\right)$

$= 792$ cm^2 (correct to 3 sig. fig.)

9. In the diagram, $ABCD$ is a square of side 4 cm. Semicircular arcs AB, BC, CD and DA have centres at the midpoints of the sides of the square. Find the area of the shaded region.

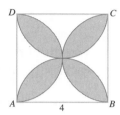

Solution

Sum of the areas of the semicircles on the sides of the square $ABCD = 4 \times \dfrac{1}{2} \times \pi \times 2^2$

$\qquad = 8\pi$ cm^2

Area of the square $ABCD = 4^2$

$\qquad = 16$ cm^2

Area of the shaded region

$= 8\pi - 16$

$= 9.13$ cm^2 (correct to 3 sig. fig.)

10. The diagram shows the cross-section of a tunnel. It is in the form of a major segment ATB of a circle with centre O and radius 4 m. Given that $\angle AOB = 90°$, find
   (a) the area of the cross-section,
   (b) the length of AB,
   (c) the perpendicular distance from the uppermost point T to AB.

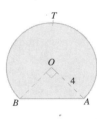

Solution

(a) Reflex $\angle AOB = 360° - 90°$

$\qquad\qquad$ ($\angle$s at a point)

$\qquad\qquad = 270°$

Area of sector $OATB = \dfrac{270}{360} \times \pi \times 4^2$

$\qquad\qquad = 12\pi$ m^2

Area of $\triangle OAB = \dfrac{1}{2} \times 4 \times 4$

$\qquad\qquad = 8$ m^2

$\therefore$ area of the cross-section

$= 12\pi + 8$

$= 45.7$ m^2 (correct to 3 sig. fig.)

(b) $AB^2 = 4^2 \times 4^2$ (Pythagoras' Theorem)

$AB = \sqrt{32}$

$= 5.66$ m   (correct to 3 sig. fig.)

(c) Since $\triangle OAB$ is a right-angled isosceles triangle,
$\angle OAB = 45°$.
Height of O above $AB = 4 \sin 45°$ m
$\therefore$ the perpendicular distance from T to AB
$= 4 + 4 \sin 45°$
$= 6.83$ m   (correct to 3 sig. fig.)

11. The diagram shows a flowerbed which is constructed from two sectors $OAPB$ and $OCQD$ of two different circles which are centred at O. $OA = 2$ m, $AD = 4$ m and $\angle AOB = 60°$. Find
(a) the perimeter of the flowerbed,
(b) the area of the flowerbed.

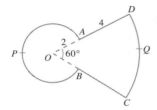

Solution
(a)   Reflex $\angle AOB = 360° - 60°$

($\angle$s at a point)

$= 300°$

Length of arc $APB = \dfrac{300}{360} \times 2\pi \times 2$

$= \dfrac{10\pi}{3}$ m

Length of arc $CQD = \dfrac{60}{360} \times 2\pi \times 6$

$= 2\pi$ m

$\therefore$ perimeter of the flowerbed

$= \dfrac{10\pi}{3} + 2\pi + 4 + 4$

$= 24.8$ m   (correct to 3 sig. fig.)

(b) Area of sector $OAPB = \dfrac{300}{360} \times \pi \times 2^2$

$= \dfrac{10\pi}{3}$ m^2

Area of sector $OCQD = \dfrac{60}{360} \times \pi \times 6^2$

$= 6\pi$ m^2

$\therefore$ area of the flowerbed

$= \dfrac{10\pi}{3} + 6\pi$

$= 29.3$ m^2 (correct to 3 sig. fig.)

Brainworks

12. A circle of radius 32 cm is divided into two parts, shaded and non-shaded, by drawing semicircles of radii 16 cm, 8 cm, 4 cm, ..., on alternate sides of the diameter of the circle as shown.
(a) What is the length of the dividing border?
(b) What is the area of each part of the circle?
(*Hint:* You may use a spreadsheet program, such as EXCEL, to solve the problem.)

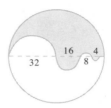

Solution
(a) Length of the dividing border

$= \left(\dfrac{1}{2} \times 2\pi \times 16 \right) + \left(\dfrac{1}{2} \times 2\pi \times 8 \right)$

$\quad + \left(\dfrac{1}{2} \times 2\pi \times 4 \right) + \left(\dfrac{1}{2} \times 2\pi \times 2 \right) + \dots$

$= (16 + 8 + 4 + 2 + \dots)\pi$

$= \dfrac{16}{1 - \frac{1}{2}} \pi$

$= 32\pi$

$= 100.5$ cm   (correct to 4 sig. fig.)

(b) Area of the shaded part

$= \left(\dfrac{1}{2} \times \pi \times 32^2 \right) - \left(\dfrac{1}{2} \times \pi \times 16^2 \right)$

$\quad + \left(\dfrac{1}{2} \times \pi \times 8^2 \right) - \left(\dfrac{1}{2} \times \pi \times 4^2 \right) + \dots$

$= (512 - 128 + 32 - 8 + \dots)\pi$

$= \dfrac{512}{1 - \left(-\frac{1}{4} \right)} \pi$

$= \dfrac{2048\pi}{5}$

$= 409.6\pi$

$= 1287$ cm^2 (correct to 4 sig. fig.)
Area of the unshaded part
$= \pi \times 32^2 - 409.6\pi$
$= 614.4\pi$
$= 1930$ cm^2 (correct to 4 sig. fig.)

Note: 1. Area of shaded part : area of unshaded part $= 2 : 3$

2. Students are not expected to know the formula for the sum of infinite geometric series. They are expected to explore this problem using a spreadsheet program.

Exercise 10.3
Basic Practice

1. In each of the following, find the angle θ subtended at the centre O by the arc of the sector. Express your answer in radians.

(a)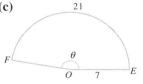

(b)

(c)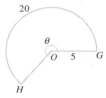

(d)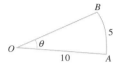

Solution

(a) $\theta = \dfrac{5}{10} = 0.5$ rad.

(b) $\theta = \dfrac{6}{4} = 1.5$ rad.

(c) $\theta = \dfrac{21}{7} = 3$ rad.

(d) $\theta = \dfrac{20}{5} = 4$ rad.

2. Express the following angles in terms of π radians.

Solution

(a) $90° = 90 \times \dfrac{\pi}{180}$ rad.

$= \dfrac{\pi}{2}$ rad.

(b) $150° = 150 \times \dfrac{\pi}{180}$ rad.

$= \dfrac{5\pi}{6}$ rad.

(c) $240° = 240 \times \dfrac{\pi}{180}$ rad.

$= \dfrac{4\pi}{3}$ rad.

(d) $330° = 330 \times \dfrac{\pi}{180}$ rad.

$= \dfrac{11\pi}{6}$ rad.

3. Express the following angles in radians, giving your answers correct to 3 significant figures.

Solution

(a) $75° = 75 \times \dfrac{\pi}{180}$ rad.

$= 1.31$ rad.   (correct to 3 sig. fig.)

(b) $140° = 140 \times \dfrac{\pi}{180}$ rad.

$= 2.44$ rad.   (correct to 3 sig. fig.)

(c) $218° = 218 \times \dfrac{\pi}{180}$ rad.

$= 3.80$ rad.   (correct to 3 sig. fig.)

(d) $316° = 316 \times \dfrac{\pi}{180}$ rad.

$= 5.52$ rad.   (correct to 3 sig. fig.)

4. Express the following angles in degrees, giving your answers correct to one decimal place.

Solution

(a) $\dfrac{\pi}{6}$ rad. $= \dfrac{\pi}{6} \times \dfrac{180°}{\pi}$

$= 30°$

(b) $\dfrac{5\pi}{4}$ rad. $= \dfrac{5\pi}{4} \times \dfrac{180°}{\pi}$

$= 225°$

(c) 2.8 rad. $= 2.8 \times \dfrac{180°}{\pi}$

$= 160.4°$ (correct to 1 d.p.)

(d) 5.7 rad. $= 5.7 \times \dfrac{180°}{\pi}$

$= 326.6°$ (correct to 1 d.p.)

5. Find the values of the following, giving your answers correct to 4 decimal places.

Solution

(a) $\sin \dfrac{\pi}{3} = 0.8660$ (correct to 4 d.p.)

(b) $\cos \dfrac{3\pi}{4} = -0.7071$ (correct to 4 d.p.)

(c) $\tan (1.2 \text{ rad.}) = 2.5722$ (correct to 4 d.p.)

(d) $\cos (2.75 \text{ rad.}) = -0.9243$ (correct to 4 d.p.)

Further Practice

6. In $\triangle ABC$, $\angle A = \dfrac{\pi}{3}$ rad. and $\angle B = \dfrac{\pi}{4}$ rad. Express $\angle C$ in terms of π radians.

Solution

$\angle C = 180° - \angle A - \angle B$ ($\angle$ sum of $\triangle$)

$= \left(\pi - \dfrac{\pi}{3} - \dfrac{\pi}{4} \right)$ rad.

$= \dfrac{5\pi}{12}$ rad.

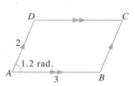

7. In a quadrilateral $ABCD$, $\angle A = 90°$, $\angle B = 72°$ and $\angle C = \frac{2\pi}{3}$ rad. Find $\angle D$

    (a) in degrees,   **(b)** in radians.

Solution

(a) $\angle C = \frac{2\pi}{3}$ rad.

$$= \frac{2\pi}{3} \times \frac{180°}{\pi}$$

$$= 120°$$

$\angle D = 360° - \angle A - \angle B - \angle C$ ($\angle$ sum of polygon)

$$= 360° - 90° - 72° - 120°$$

$$= 78°$$

(b) $\angle D = 78 \times \frac{\pi}{180}$ rad.

$$= 1.36 \text{ rad.} \quad \text{(correct to 3 sig. fig.)}$$

8. In the diagram, $AC = 12$ cm, $\angle BAC = 0.7$ rad. and $\angle ABC = \frac{\pi}{2}$ rad. Find

    (a) the length of BC,

    (b) the length of AB.

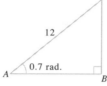

Solution

(a) $BC = AC \sin \angle BAC$

$$= 12 \sin (0.7 \text{ rad.})$$

$$= 7.73 \text{ cm} \quad \text{(correct to 3 sig. fig.)}$$

(b) $AB = AC \cos \angle BAC$

$$= 12 \cos (0.7 \text{ rad.})$$

$$= 9.18 \text{ cm} \quad \text{(correct to 3 sig. fig.)}$$

9. In $\triangle ABC$, $AB = 4$ cm, $BC = 5$ cm and $AC = 8$ cm. Find $\angle ABC$ in radians.

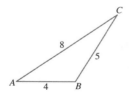

Solution

Using the cosine rule,

$$\cos \angle ABC = \frac{4^2 + 5^2 - 8^2}{2 \times 4 \times 5}$$

$$= -\frac{23}{40}$$

$\angle ABC = 2.18$ rad.   (correct to 3 sig. fig.)

Maths@Work

10. The diagram shows a parallelogram board $ABCD$. $AB = 3$ m, $AD = 2$ m and $\angle BAD = 1.2$ rad. Find

    (a) $\angle ABC$ in radians,

    (b) the perpendicular height from D to AB,

    (c) the area of the board.

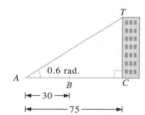

Solution

(a) $\angle ABC = (\pi - 1.2)$ rad.   (int. $\angle$s, $AD \parallel BC$)

       $= 1.94$ rad.   (correct to 3 sig. fig.)

(b) Perpendicular height from D to AB

$$= 2 \sin (1.2 \text{ rad.})$$

$$= 1.864$$

$$= 1.86 \text{ m} \quad \text{(correct to 3 sig. fig.)}$$

(c) Area of the board

$$= 3 \times 1.864$$

$$= 5.59 \text{ m}^2 \quad \text{(correct to 3 sig. fig.)}$$

11.

In the diagram, TC is a vertical building and A is a point at ground level and 75 m from the building. The angle of elevation of the top T of the building from A is 0.6 rad.

    (a) Find the height of the building.

    (b) B is a point on AC such that $AB = 30$ m. Find the angle of elevation of T from B, giving your answer in radians correct to 2 decimal places.

Solution

(a) $TC = 75 \tan (0.6 \text{ rad.})$

$$= 51.31$$

$$= 51.3 \text{ m} \quad \text{(correct to 3 sig. fig.)}$$

The height of the building is 51.3 m.

(b) $BC = 75 - 30$

$$= 45 \text{ m}$$

$$\tan \angle TBC = \frac{51.31}{45}$$

$$\angle TBC = 0.85 \text{ rad.} \quad \text{(correct to 2 d.p.)}$$

Brainworks

12. (a) Using your calculator, copy and complete the following table, giving the answers correct to 5 decimal places.

θ (rad.)	0.1	0.05	0.01	0.001	0.000 1
$\sin\theta$	0.099 83	0.049 98	0.010 00	0.001 00	0.000 10
$\dfrac{\sin\theta}{\theta}$	0.998 33	0.999 58	0.999 98	1.000 00	1.000 00

(b) What can you say about the value of $\dfrac{\sin\theta}{\theta}$ when θ is a very, very small angle in radians?

Solution

(b) $\dfrac{\sin\theta}{\theta}$ approaches 1 when θ is a very, very small angle in radians.

Exercise 10.4

Basic Practice

1. Find the length of the arc AB and the area of the sector OAB in each of the following. The unit of length is cm in each case.

(a) 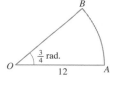   **(b)**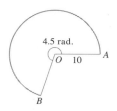

Solution

(a) Length of arc $AB = 12 \times \dfrac{3}{4}$

$= 9$ cm

Area of sector $OAB = \dfrac{1}{2} \times 12^2 \times \dfrac{3}{4}$

$= 54$ cm^2

(b) Length of arc $AB = 10 \times 4.5$

$= 45$ cm

Area of sector $OAB = \dfrac{1}{2} \times 10^2 \times 4.5$

$= 225$ cm^2

2. Copy and complete the following table for the sectors of circles.

	Radius	Angle at centre (rad.)	Arc Length	Area of Sector
(a)	4 cm		6 cm	
(b)	1.5 m			0.75 m^2
(c)		2.5 rad.	20 cm	
(d)			5 m	6 m^2

Solution

(a)

$$4\theta = 6$$
$$\theta = 1.5 \text{ rad.}$$

Area of sector $= \dfrac{1}{2} \times 4 \times 6$

$= 12$ cm^2

(b) $\dfrac{1}{2} \times 1.5^2 \times \theta = 0.75$

$$\theta = \dfrac{2}{3} \text{ rad.}$$

Arc length $= 1.5 \times \dfrac{2}{3}$ rad.

$= 1$ m

(c) $r \times 2.5 = 20$

$r = 8$

$\therefore$ radius $= 8$ cm

Area of sector $= \dfrac{1}{2} \times 8^2 \times 2.5$

$= 80$ cm^2

(d) $r\theta = 5$ .... (1)

$\dfrac{1}{2}r^2\theta = 6$ .... (2)

From (1), $\theta = \dfrac{5}{r}$ .... (3)

Put (3) into (2),

$$\dfrac{1}{2}r^2\left(\dfrac{5}{r}\right) = 6$$
$$r = \dfrac{12}{5}$$
$$= 2.4$$

$\therefore$ radius $= 2.4$ cm

Put $r = 2.4$ into (1),

$$2.4\theta = 5$$
$$\theta = 2.08 \text{ rad.} \quad \left(\text{or } 2\dfrac{1}{12} \text{ rad.}\right)$$

Further Practice

3. In the diagram, O is the centre of the circle, $\angle AOB = \dfrac{2\pi}{3}$ rad. and the length of the arc APB is 8π cm. Find

(a) the radius of the circle,
(b) the area of the sector $OAPB$,
(c) the length of the arc AQB,
(d) the area of the sector $OAQB$.

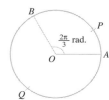

Solution

(a) Let r cm be the radius of the circle.

$$r \times \frac{2\pi}{3} = 8\pi$$
$$r = 12$$

∴ the radius is 12 cm.

(b) Area of sector $OAPB$

$$= \frac{1}{2} \times 12^2 \times \frac{2\pi}{3}$$
$$= 48\pi$$
$$= 151 \text{ cm}^2 \quad \text{(correct to 3 sig. fig.)}$$

(c) Reflex $\angle AOB = \left(2\pi - \frac{2\pi}{3}\right)$ rad.

$$= \frac{4\pi}{3} \text{ rad.}$$

Length of arc AQB

$$= 12 \times \frac{4\pi}{3}$$
$$= 16\pi$$
$$= 50.3 \text{ cm} \quad \text{(correct to 3 sig. fig.)}$$

(d) Area of sector $OAQB$

$$= \frac{1}{2} \times 12^2 \times \frac{4\pi}{3}$$
$$= 96\pi$$
$$= 302 \text{ cm}^2 \quad \text{(correct to 3 sig. fig.)}$$

4. A minor arc PQ of a circle, with centre O and radius 18 cm, is 12 cm long. Find $\angle POQ$ in radians and the area of the minor sector OPQ.

Solution

Let $\angle POQ = \theta$ radians.
$$18\theta = 12$$
$$\theta = \frac{2}{3}$$
∴ $\angle POQ = \frac{2}{3}$ rad.

Area of minor sector $OPQ = \frac{1}{2} \times 18^2 \times \frac{2}{3}$
$$= 108 \text{ cm}^2$$

5. A sector cut from a circle of radius 10 cm has a perimeter of 36 cm. Find
(a) the angle subtended at the centre by the arc of the sector,
(b) the area of the sector.

Solution

(a) Length of arc on the sector $= 36 - 10$
$$= 16 \text{ cm}$$
Let θ rad. be the angle subtended at the centre.
$$10\theta = 16$$
$$\theta = 1.6$$
∴ the required angle is 1.6 rad.

(b) Area of the sector $= \frac{1}{2} \times 10^2 \times 1.6$
$$= 80 \text{ cm}^2$$

6. In the diagram, the shaded region is formed by the sectors OAD and OBC. $OA = 8$ cm, $AB = 12$ cm and the area of the sector OAD is 80 cm². Find
(a) $\angle AOD$ in radians,
(b) the perimeter of the shaded region,
(c) the area of the shaded region.

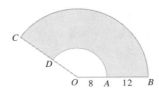

Solution

(a) Let $\angle AOD = \theta$ radians.
$$\frac{1}{2} \times 8^2 \times \theta = 80$$
$$\theta = 2.5$$
i.e. $\angle AOD = 2.5$ rad.

(b) Length of arc $AD = 8 \times 2.5$
$$= 20 \text{ cm}$$
Length of arc $BC = 20 \times 2.5$
$$= 50 \text{ cm}$$
∴ perimeter of the shaded region
$$= 20 + 50 + 12 + 12$$
$$= 94 \text{ cm}$$

(c) Area of sector $OBC = \frac{1}{2} \times 20^2 \times 2.5$
$$= 500 \text{ cm}^2$$
∴ area of shaded region $= 500 - 80$
$$= 420 \text{ cm}^2$$

7. The diagram shows a semicircle with centre O. $OB = 20$ cm and $\angle ABC = 0.6$ rad. Find
(a) the perimeter of the segment AQC,
(b) the area of the segment AQC,
(c) the area of the segment BPC.

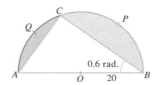

Solution

(a) Draw the radius OC.

$\angle AOC = 2\angle ABC$ ($\angle$ at centre $= 2\angle$ at circumference)

$\qquad = 2 \times 0.6$ rad.

$\qquad = 1.2$ rad.

Length of arc $AQC = 20 \times 1.2$

$\qquad\qquad\qquad = 24$ cm

$\angle ACB = 90°$ ($\angle$ in a semicircle)

$AC = AB \sin (0.6$ rad.$)$

$\quad = 40 \sin (0.6$ rad.$)$

$\quad = 22.586$ cm

$\therefore$ perimeter of segment AQC

$\quad = 24 + 22.586$

$\quad = 46.6$ cm (correct to 3 sig. fig.)

(b) Area of sector $OAQC = \frac{1}{2} \times 20^2 \times 1.2$

$\qquad\qquad\qquad\qquad = 240$ cm^2

Area of $\triangle OAC = \frac{1}{2} \times 20 \times 20 \times \sin (1.2$ rad.$)$

$\qquad\qquad\qquad = 186.41$ cm^2

$\therefore$ area of segment AQC

$\quad = 240 - 186.41$

$\quad = 53.6$ cm^2 (correct to 3 sig. fig.)

(c) Area of the semicircle $= \frac{1}{2} \times \pi \times 20^2$

$\qquad\qquad\qquad\qquad = 200\pi$ cm^2

Area of $\triangle BOC = \frac{1}{2} \times 20^2 \times \sin (\pi - 1.2)$

$\qquad\qquad\qquad = 186.41$ cm^2

$\therefore$ area of segment BPC

$\quad =$ area of the semicircle $-$ area of sector $OAQC$

$\qquad -$ area of $\triangle BOC$

$\quad = 200\pi - 240 - 186.41$

$\quad = 202$ cm^2 (correct to 3 sig. fig.)

Maths@Work

8. In the figure, O is the centre of a circular cake of radius 15 cm. It is cut into two segments by a chord AB which is 24 cm long. Find

(a) $\angle AOB$ in radians,

(b) the area of $\triangle AOB$,

(c) the area of the major segment AQB.

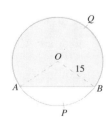

Solution

(a) Draw a perpendicular ON from O to AB.

Then $\quad BN = \frac{1}{2} \times 24$

$\qquad\qquad = 12$ cm

$\sin \angle BON = \frac{12}{15}$

$\angle BON = 0.9273$ rad.

$\therefore \quad \angle AOB = 2 \times \angle BON$

$\qquad\qquad = 1.8546$ rad.

$\qquad\qquad = 1.85$ rad. (correct to 3 sig. fig.)

(b) Area of $\triangle AOB$

$\quad = \frac{1}{2} \times 15 \times 15 \times \sin (1.8546$ rad.$)$

$\quad = 108.0$ cm^2

$\quad = 108$ cm^2 (correct to 3 sig. fig.)

(c) Area of sector $OAQB = \frac{1}{2} \times 15^2 \times (2\pi - 1.8546)$

$\qquad\qquad\qquad\qquad = 498.2$ cm^2

$\therefore$ area of major segment AQB

$\quad = 108.0 + 498.2$

$\quad = 606$ cm^2 (correct to 3 sig. fig.)

9. The diagram shows two concentric circles with a common centre O. Their radii are 8 cm and 16 cm respectively. AB is a tangent to the inner circle at T. Find

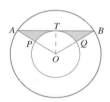

(a) $\angle AOB$ in radians,

(b) the length of AB,

(c) the area of the shaded region.

Solution

(a) $\qquad \angle ATO = 90°$ (tangent $\perp$ radius)

$\cos \angle AOT = \frac{OT}{OA}$

$\qquad\qquad\quad = \frac{8}{16}$

$\angle AOT = \frac{\pi}{3}$ rad.

$\angle AOB = 2\angle AOT$

$\qquad\quad = \frac{2\pi}{3}$ rad.

$\qquad\quad = 2.09$ rad. (correct to 3 sig. fig.)

(b) $AT^2 = 16^2 - 8^2$

$AT = \sqrt{192}$ cm

$AB = 2AT$

$\qquad = 2\sqrt{192}$

$\qquad = 27.7$ cm (correct to 3 sig. fig.)

(c) Area of $\triangle OAB = \frac{1}{2} \times 16^2 \times \sin \frac{2\pi}{3}$

$= 110.85 \text{ cm}^2$

Area of sector $OPTQ = \frac{1}{2} \times 8^2 \times \frac{2\pi}{3}$

$= 67.02 \text{ cm}^2$

∴ area of the shaded region

$= 110.85 - 67.02$

$= 43.8 \text{ cm}^2$ (correct to 3 sig. fig.)

10. An artist draws a crescent *BPCQ* as shown. *BQC* is an arc of the circle with centre *O* and radius 20 cm. *BPC* is an arc with centre *A* on the circle, and $\angle BAC = 1.3$ rad. Find

(a) $\angle BOC$ in radians,

(b) the length of *AB*,

(c) the perimeter of the crescent,

(d) the area of the crescent.

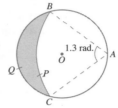

Solution

(a) $\angle BOC$

$= 2\angle BAC$ (∠ at centre = 2∠ at circumference)

$= 2 \times 1.3$ rad.

$= 2.6$ rad.

(b) $\angle OAB = \frac{1}{2} \times 1.3$ rad.

$= 0.65$ rad.

$\frac{1}{2} AB = OA \cos \angle OAB$

$AB = 2 \times 20 \times \cos (0.65 \text{ rad.})$

$= 31.84$

$= 31.8$ cm (correct to 3 sig. fig.)

(c) Length of arc $BPC = 31.84 \times 1.3$

$= 41.392$ cm

Length of arc $BQC = 20 \times 2.6$

$= 52$ cm

∴ perimeter of the crescent

$= 41.392 + 52$

$= 93.4$ cm (correct to 3 sig. fig.)

(d) Area of sector $ABPC = \frac{1}{2} \times 31.84^2 \times 1.3$

$= 658.96 \text{ cm}^2$

Area of sector $OBQC = \frac{1}{2} \times 20^2 \times 2.6$

$= 520 \text{ cm}^2$

Area of $\triangle OAB$

$= \frac{1}{2} \times 20^2 \times \sin (\pi - 1.3)$ rad.

$= 192.71 \text{ cm}^2$

Similarly,

Area of $\triangle OAC = 192.71 \text{ cm}^2$

Area of the crescent

= area of sector $OBQC$ − (area of sector $ABPC$ − area of $\triangle OAB$ − area of $\triangle OAC$)

$= 520 - (658.96 - 192.71 - 192.71)$

$= 246.46$

$= 246 \text{ cm}^2$ (correct to 3 sig. fig.)

11.

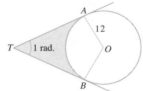

In the diagram, *TA* and *TB* are tangents to the circle, centre *O*, at *A* and *B* respectively. $OA = 12$ cm and $\angle ATB = 1$ rad. Find

(a) $\angle AOB$ in radians,

(b) the length of *AT*,

(c) the perimeter of the shaded region,

(d) the area of the shaded region.

Solution

(a) $\angle OAT = \frac{\pi}{2}$ rad. (tangent ⊥ radius)

$\angle AOB$

$= \left(2\pi - 1 - \frac{\pi}{2} - \frac{\pi}{2} \right)$ rad. (∠ sum of polygon)

$= (\pi - 1)$ rad.

$= 2.14$ rad. (correct to 3 sig. fig.)

(b) Join *O* and *T*.

$\angle OTA = \frac{1}{2} \angle ATB$

$= \frac{1}{2}$ rad.

$\tan \angle OTA = \frac{OA}{AT}$

∴ $AT = \dfrac{12}{\tan \left(\frac{1}{2} \text{ rad.} \right)}$

$= 21.966$

$= 22.0$ cm (correct to 3 sig. fig.)

(c) Length of minor arc $AB = 12 \times (\pi - 1)$

$= 25.699$ cm

∴ perimeter of the shaded region

$= 25.699 + 2 \times 21.966$

$= 69.6$ cm (correct to 3 sig. fig.)

(d)
$$\text{Area of } \triangle OAT = \frac{1}{2} \times 12 \times 21.966$$
$$= 131.796 \text{ cm}^2$$
$$\text{Area of minor sector } OAB = \frac{1}{2} \times 12^2 \times (\pi - 1)$$
$$= 154.195 \text{ cm}^2$$

Area of the shaded region
= 2(area of $\triangle OAT$) – area of minor sector OAB
= (2 × 131.796) – (154.195)
= 109 cm^2 (correct to 3 sig. fig.)

12.

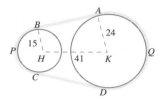

The diagram shows two wheels of radii 15 cm and 24 cm. Their centres, H and K, are 41 cm apart. A driving belt $ABPCDQ$ is mounted on the two wheels such that AB and CD are common tangents to the two wheels. Find

(a) $\angle AKH$ in radians,
(b)   the length of AB,
(c)   the length of the driving belt.

Solution
(a)   Draw a perpendicular HN from H to AK.
$$KN = 24 - 15$$
$$= 9 \text{ cm}$$
$$\cos \angle AKH = \frac{KN}{HK}$$
$$= \frac{9}{41}$$
$$\angle AKH = 1.3495 \text{ rad.}$$
$$= 1.35 \text{ rad.}   \text{(correct to 3 sig. fig.)}$$
(b) $AB = HN$
$$= \sqrt{41^2 - 9^2}   \text{(Pythagoras' Theorem)}$$
$$= 40 \text{ cm}$$
(c) $$\angle BHP = 2\angle AKH$$
$$\text{(corr. } \angle \text{s, } BH \text{ // } AK)$$
$$\angle BHC = 2\angle AKN$$
$$= 2 \times 1.3495 \text{ rad.}$$
$$= 2.699 \text{ rad.}$$
Length of arc BPC = 15 × 2.699
$$= 40.485 \text{ cm}$$
Reflex $\angle AKD = 2\pi - 2 \times \angle AKH$
$$= (2\pi - 2 \times 1.3495) \text{ rad.}$$
$$= 3.584 \text{ rad.}$$
Length of arc AQD = 24 × 3.584
$$= 86.016 \text{ cm}$$
∴ length of the driving belt
= 40.485 + 86.016 + 40 + 40
= 207 cm   (correct to 3 sig. fig.)

Brainworks

13.   A piece of wire is 100 cm long. It is bent into a sector OAB of a circle with radius r cm as shown. Find the radius of the circle which gives the maximum area of sector OAB.

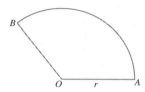

Solution
$$\text{Arc } AB = 100 - r - r$$
$$= (100 - 2r) \text{ cm}$$
$$\text{Area of the sector } OAB = \frac{1}{2} \times r \times (100 - 2r)$$
$$= 50r - r^2$$
$$= -(r^2 - 50r + 25^2) + 25^2$$
$$= -(r - 25)^2 + 625$$
Hence, the maximum area of the sector is 625 cm^2 when the radius is 25 cm.

Note: Students may try to find the maximum area by evaluating the areas of the sectors for various radii with the aid of a spreadsheet program.

Revision Exercise 10

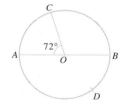

1.   In the figure, AB is a diameter of the circle with centre O, $\angle AOC = 72°$ and the minor arc $AC = 15$ cm. Find
   (a)   the length of the arc BC,
   (b)   the length of the semicircular arc ADB,
   (c)   the radius of the circle,
   (d)   the ratio of the areas of sectors OAC and OBC.

Solution
(a) $\angle BOC = 180° - 72°$ (adj. $\angle$s on a st. line)
$$= 108°$$
$$\text{Length of arc } BC = \frac{108}{72} \times 15$$
$$= 22.5 \text{ cm}$$
(b)   Length of semicircular arc ADB = 15 + 22.5
$$= 37.5 \text{ cm}$$
(c)   Let r cm be the radius of the circle.
$$\pi r = 37.5$$
$$r = 11.9   \text{(correct to 3 sig. fig.)}$$
∴ the radius is 11.9 cm.

(d) Area of sector OAC : area of sector OBC
$= \angle AOC : \angle BOC$
$= 72 : 108$
$= 2 : 3$

2. In the diagram, AB and CD are two parallel chords of the circle with centre O. $\angle AOB = 90°$, $\angle COD = 120°$ and the minor arc $BC = 25\pi$ cm. Find
(a) the radius of the circle,
(b) the area of the sector OBC,
(c) the area of $\triangle OCD$.

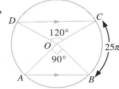

Solution
(a) By symmetry,
$\angle BOC = \angle AOD$
Hence,
$\angle BOC = \frac{1}{2}(360° - 120° - 90°)$ ($\angle$s at a point)
$= 75°$

Let r cm be the radius of the circle.
$\frac{75}{360} \times 2\pi \times r = 25\pi$
$r = \frac{25 \times 360}{75 \times 2}$
$= 60$
$\therefore$ the radius is 60 cm.

(b) Area of sector OBC
$= \frac{1}{2} \times 60^2 \times \frac{75\pi}{180}$
$= 750\pi$
$= 2360$ cm^2 (correct to 3 sig. fig.)

(c) Area of $\triangle OCD$
$= \frac{1}{2} \times 60^2 \times \sin 120°$
$= 1560$ cm^2 (correct to 3 sig. fig.)

3. The figure shown is formed by a part of a rectangle $ABCD$, and a part of a circle with centre A and radius AD. $CD = 8$ cm and the area of $ABCD = 32$ cm^2. Find
(a) the length of the arc DEF,
(b) the perimeter of the figure,
(c) the area of the figure.

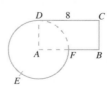

Solution
(a) $AD = 32 \div 8$
$= 4$ cm
Reflex $\angle DEF = 360° - 90°$ ($\angle$s at a point)
$= 270°$

Length of arc DEF
$= \frac{270}{360} \times 2\pi \times 4$
$= 6\pi$
$= 18.8$ cm   (correct to 3 sig. fig.)

(b) Perimeter of the figure
$= 6\pi + 8 + 4 + 4$
$= 16 + 6\pi$
$= 34.8$ cm   (correct to 3 sig. fig.)

(c) Area of sector $ADEF = \frac{270}{360} \times \pi \times 4^2$
$= 12\pi$ cm^2
$\therefore$ area of the figure
$= 12\pi + 32$
$= 69.7$ cm^2 (correct to 3 sig. fig.)

4. The diagram shows six shaded petals that meet at the centre O of a circle of radius 3 cm. The shaded petals are formed by equal arcs of six circles, each of radius 3 cm. Find
(a) the total perimeter of the six petals,
(b) the total area of the six petals.

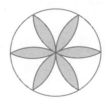

Solution
(a)

Consider a half of a petal as shown above. It is the minor segment OBP and $\triangle OAB$ is equilateral. Hence, $\angle OAB = 60°$.

Length of arc $OPB = \frac{60}{360} \times 2\pi \times 3$
$= \pi$ cm
$\therefore$ total perimeter of the six petals
$= 6 \times (2 \times \pi)$
$= 12\pi$
$= 37.7$ cm   (correct to 3 sig. fig.)

(b) Area of sector $AOPB = \dfrac{60}{360} \times \pi \times 3^2$

$= 1.5\pi$ cm^2

Area of $\triangle AOB = \dfrac{1}{2} \times 3 \times 3 \times \sin 60°$

$= \dfrac{9\sqrt{3}}{4}$ cm^2

$\therefore$ area of segment $OPB = \left(1.5\pi - \dfrac{9\sqrt{3}}{4}\right)$ cm^2

Total area of the six petals

$= 6 \times 2 \times \left(1.5\pi - \dfrac{9\sqrt{3}}{4}\right)$

$= 9.78$ cm^2 (correct to 3 sig. fig.)

5. The figure shown is formed by arcs of two circles with centres at A and B respectively. The radius of each circle is 12 cm and the length of AB is 12 cm. Find
(a) the perimeter of the figure,
(b) the area of the figure.

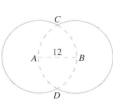

Solution

(a) $\triangle ABC$ is equilateral.

$\therefore \angle BAC = 60°$

Length of minor arc $BC = \dfrac{60}{360} \times 2\pi \times 12$

$= 4\pi$ cm

Length of major arc CD of a circle
$= (2\pi \times 12) - (2 \times 4\pi)$
$= 16\pi$ cm

$\therefore$ perimeter of the figure
$= 2 \times 16\pi$
$= 32\pi$
$= 101$ cm (correct to 3 sig. fig.)

(b) Area of $\triangle ACD = \dfrac{1}{2} \times 12 \times 12 \times \sin 120°$

$= 62.354$ cm^2

Area of major sector $ACD = \dfrac{240}{360} \times \pi \times 12^2$

$= 301.59$ cm^2

$\therefore$ area of the figure
$= 2 \times (62.354 + 301.59)$
$= 728$ cm^2 (correct to 3 sig. fig.)

6. In the diagram, $ABCD$ is a quadrilateral. $\angle A = 1.2$ rad., $\angle B = 1.4$ rad. and $\angle D = 2.1$ rad.

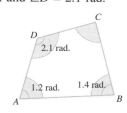

(a) Find $\angle BCD$
  (i) in radians,
  (ii) in degrees.
(b) If a sector of radius 5 cm is drawn with the centre at each vertex of the quadrilateral as shown, find
  (i) the total area of the four sectors,
  (ii) the area of the sector at the vertex A.

Solution

(a) **(i)** $\angle BCD = 2\pi - 1.2 - 1.4 - 2.1$

$\qquad\qquad$ ($\angle$ sum of polygon)

$= 1.583$

$= 1.58$ rad. (correct to 3 sig. fig.)

(ii) $\angle BCD = 1.583 \times \dfrac{180°}{\pi}$

$= 90.7°$ (correct to 1 d.p.)

(b) **(i)** Total area of the four sectors
$=$ area of a circle of radius 5 cm
$= \pi \times 5^2$
$= 25\pi$
$= 78.5$ cm^2 (correct to 3 sig. fig.)

(ii) Area of the sector at vertex A

$= \dfrac{1}{2} \times 5^2 \times 1.2$

$= 15$ cm^2

7. In the diagram, a circle with centre G and radius 5 cm is inscribed inside the sector ABC. Given that $\angle BAC = \dfrac{\pi}{3}$ rad., find
(a) the radius of the sector ABC,
(b) the length of the arc BC,
(c) the area of the shaded region.

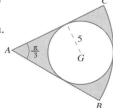

Solution

(a) $\angle CAG = \angle BAG$

$(AC = AB$, tangents from ext. point)

$\angle CAG = \dfrac{1}{2} \times \dfrac{\pi}{3}$ rad.

$= \dfrac{\pi}{6}$ rad.

$\dfrac{5}{AG} = \sin \angle CAG$

$\dfrac{5}{AG} = \sin \dfrac{\pi}{6}$

$\dfrac{5}{AG} = \dfrac{1}{2}$

$AG = 10$ cm

$\therefore$ radius of the sector $= 10 + 5 = 15$ cm

(b) Length of arc BC

$$= 15 \times \frac{\pi}{3}$$
$$= 5\pi$$
$$= 15.7 \text{ cm} \quad \text{(correct to 3 sig. fig.)}$$

(c) Area of sector $ABC = \frac{1}{2} \times 15^2 \times \frac{\pi}{3}$

$$= \frac{75\pi}{2} \text{ cm}^2$$

Area of the circle with centre $G = \pi \times 5^2$
$$= 25\pi \text{ cm}^2$$

$\therefore$ area of the shaded region
$$= \frac{75\pi}{2} - 25\pi$$
$$= 12.5\pi$$
$$= 39.3 \text{ cm}^2 \quad \text{(correct to 3 sig. fig.)}$$

8. In the diagram, OAD and OBC are two sectors of two circles with radii 10 cm and 25 cm respectively. Given that arc $AD = 22$ cm, find
(a) $\angle AOD$ in radians,
(b) the length of the arc BC,
(c) the area of the shaded region.

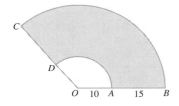

Solution
(a) Let $\angle AOD = \theta$ rad.
$$10\theta = 22$$
$$\theta = 2.2$$
$\therefore \quad \angle AOD = 2.2$ rad.

(b) Length of arc $BC = 25 \times 2.2$
$$= 55 \text{ cm}$$

(c) Area of sector $OBC = \frac{1}{2} \times 25^2 \times 2.2$
$$= 687.5 \text{ cm}^2$$

Area of sector $OAD = \frac{1}{2} \times 10^2 \times 2.2$
$$= 110 \text{ cm}^2$$

$\therefore$ area of the shaded region $= 687.5 - 110$
$$= 577.5 \text{ cm}^2$$

9. In the diagram, TA and TB are tangents to a circle, centre O, at A and B respectively. $\angle ACB = 56°$ and $TA = 9$ cm.

Find
(a) $\angle ATB$,
(b) the radius of the circle,
(c) the length of the arc AB,
(d) the area of the shaded region.

Solution
(a) Draw the radii OA and OB.
$$\angle AOB = 2 \times 56° \quad (\angle \text{ at centre} = 2\angle \text{ at}$$
$$\text{circumference})$$
$$= 112°$$
$$\angle OAT = \angle OBT = 90° \quad (\text{tangent} \perp \text{radius})$$
$$\therefore \quad \angle ATB = 360° - 112° - 90° - 90°$$
$$(\angle \text{ sum of polygon})$$
$$= 68°$$

(b) $\angle OTA = \frac{1}{2} \times 68°$
$$= 34°$$
$$\frac{OA}{AT} = \tan \angle OTA$$
$$\frac{OA}{9} = \tan 34°$$
$$OA = 6.0706$$
$$= 6.07 \text{ cm} \quad \text{(correct to 3 sig. fig.)}$$
$\therefore$ radius of the circle is 6.07 cm.

(c) Length of arc AB
$$= \frac{112}{360} \times 2\pi \times 6.0706$$
$$= 11.9 \text{ cm} \quad \text{(correct to 3 sig. fig.)}$$

(d) Area of $\triangle OAT = \frac{1}{2} \times 6.0706 \times 9$
$$= 27.3177 \text{ cm}^2$$
Area of sector $OAB = \frac{112}{360} \times \pi \times 6.0706^2$
$$= 36.0187 \text{ cm}^2$$
$\therefore$ area of the shaded region
$$= (2 \times 27.3177) - 36.0187$$
$$= 18.6 \text{ cm}^2 \quad \text{(correct to 3 sig. fig.)}$$

10. In the diagram, three circles with respective centres A, B and C, touch one another. The radii of the circles are 3 cm, 2 cm and 1 cm respectively.

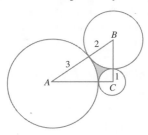

Find
(a) the angles of $\triangle ABC$ in radians,
(b) the perimeter of the shaded region,
(c) the area of $\triangle ABC$,
(d) the area of the shaded region.

Solution

(a)
$$AC = 3 + 1$$
$$= 4 \text{ cm}$$
$$BC = 2 + 1$$
$$= 3 \text{ cm}$$
$$AB = 3 + 2$$
$$= 5 \text{ cm}$$
$$AC^2 + BC^2 = 4^2 + 3^2$$
$$= 5^2$$
$$\therefore \ AC^2 + BC^2 = AB^2$$
$$\angle ACB = \frac{\pi}{2} \text{ rad.} \quad \text{(converse of Pythagoras'}$$
$$\text{Theorem)}$$
$$= 1.57 \text{ rad. (correct to 3 sig. fig.)}$$
$$\sin \angle BAC = \frac{3}{5}$$
$$\angle BAC = 0.6435 \text{ rad.}$$
$$= 0.644 \text{ rad.}$$
$$\text{(correct to 3 sig. fig.)}$$
$$\angle ABC = \left(\pi - \frac{\pi}{2} - 0.6435 \right) \text{ rad.}$$
$$(\angle \text{ sum of } \triangle)$$
$$= 0.9273 \text{ rad.}$$
$$= 0.927 \text{ rad.}$$
$$\text{(correct to 3 sig. fig.)}$$

(b) Perimeter of the shaded region
$$= 3 \times 0.6435 + 2 \times 0.9273 + 1 \times \frac{\pi}{2}$$
$$= 5.36 \text{ cm} \quad \text{(correct to 3 sig. fig.)}$$

(c) Area of $\triangle ABC = \frac{1}{2} \times 4 \times 3$
$$= 6 \text{ cm}^2$$

(d) Sum of the areas of the 3 sectors within $\triangle ABC$
$$= \left(\frac{1}{2} \times 3^2 \times 0.6435 \right) + \left(\frac{1}{2} \times 2^2 \times 0.9273 \right)$$
$$+ \left(\frac{1}{2} \times 1^2 \times \frac{\pi}{2} \right)$$
$$= 5.5357 \text{ cm}^2$$

$\therefore$ area of the shaded region
$$= 6 - 5.5357$$
$$= 0.464 \text{ cm}^2 \quad \text{(correct to 3 sig. fig.)}$$

Chapter 11   Quartiles And Percentiles

Class Activity 1

Consider the following histogram which shows the daily wages of 50 workers.

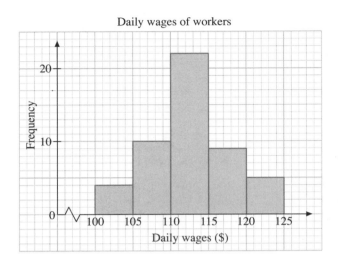

1. Copy and complete the following frequency table corresponding to the histogram.

Daily wages (x)	Frequency
$100 < x \leqslant 105$	4
$105 < x \leqslant 110$	10
$110 < x \leqslant 115$	22
$115 < x \leqslant 120$	9
$120 < x \leqslant 125$	5

2. (a)   Find the number of workers with wages less than or equal to

(a) $105,   \underline{\quad 4 \quad}$.

(b) $110,   \underline{\quad 14 \quad}$.

(c) $115,   \underline{\quad 36 \quad}$.

3. Can you find the exact number of workers with wages $\leqslant$ 118?

No, we can only estimate.

Extend Your Learning Curve

Percentile Score and Examination Report

The following data shows the scores of 80 students in a Mathematics examination.

$$
\begin{array}{cccccccccc}
63 & 59 & 69 & 61 & 71 & 61 & 58 & 39 & 90 & 64 \\
71 & 66 & 41 & 51 & 61 & 66 & 59 & 74 & 78 & 38 \\
51 & 54 & 61 & 46 & 51 & 88 & 68 & 63 & 58 & 59 \\
59 & 34 & 44 & 90 & 61 & 51 & 61 & 68 & 44 & 41 \\
52 & 59 & 54 & 74 & 78 & 48 & 75 & 39 & 54 & 43 \\
33 & 54 & 43 & 63 & 46 & 41 & 38 & 47 & 30 & 79 \\
66 & 57 & 82 & 63 & 51 & 58 & 77 & 48 & 43 & 60 \\
66 & 22 & 51 & 67 & 81 & 78 & 34 & 46 & 62 & 53 \\
\end{array}
$$

(a) Construct a frequency table with uniform class intervals starting with $20 < x \leq 30$.
(b) Draw a cumulative frequency curve for the data.
(c) If the score of a student is 61, what is the percentile score of the student?
(d) Write a brief report to describe some statistics of the scores of the distribution.

Solution

(a) The following is the required frequency table for the data.

Score (x)	Tally	Frequency
$20 < x \leq 30$	//	2
$30 < x \leq 40$	### //	7
$40 < x \leq 50$	### ### ////	14
$50 < x \leq 60$	### ### ### ### //	22
$60 < x \leq 70$	### ### ### ###	20
$70 < x \leq 80$	### ###	10
$80 < x \leq 90$	###	5
Total		80

(b) First we set up a cumulative frequency table.

Score (x)	Cumulative Frequency
$x \leq 20$	0
$x \leq 30$	2
$x \leq 40$	9
$x \leq 50$	23
$x \leq 60$	45
$x \leq 70$	65
$x \leq 80$	75
$x \leq 90$	80

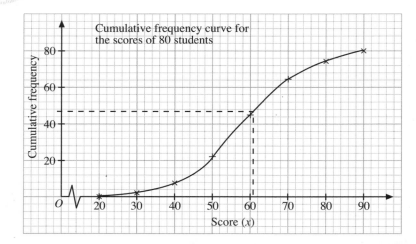

(c) From the cumulative frequency curve,

number of students with score $\leqslant 61 = 48$

$\therefore$ percentile score of the students $= \dfrac{48}{80} \times 100\%$

$\qquad\qquad\qquad\qquad\qquad\qquad\quad = 60\%$

(d) The scores of the students range from 22 to 90, i.e. the range is 68.
The median score of students is 58.

25% of students have scores less than or equal to 48, while 75% of students have scores less than or equal to 66. Thus, the interquartile range of the scores is 18.

Besides, the top 10% of students have scores greater than or equal to 77.

The distribution of the scores is fairly symmetrical, with the highest frequency in the middle class.

Try It!

Section 11.1

1. The following table shows the lengths of 80 screws produced by a machine.

Length (x mm)	$30 < x \leqslant 32$	$32 < x \leqslant 34$	$34 < x \leqslant 36$	$36 < x \leqslant 38$	$38 < x \leqslant 40$	$40 < x \leqslant 42$
Frequency	5	16	21	18	12	8

(a) Construct the cumulative frequency table for the data.

(b) Draw a cumulative frequency curve for the data.

(c) Estimate the percentage of screws which are longer than 39 mm.

Solution

1. (a)

Length (x mm)	Cumulative Frequency
$\leqslant 30$	0
$\leqslant 32$	5
$\leqslant 34$	21
$\leqslant 36$	42
$\leqslant 38$	60
$\leqslant 40$	72
$\leqslant 42$	80

(b) The following diagram shows the cumulative frequency curve for the data.

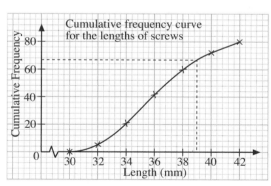

(c) Number of screws shorter than or equal to 39 mm = 66

∴ percentage of screws longer than 39 mm

$$= \frac{80 - 66}{80} \times 100\%$$

$$= 17.5\%$$

Section 11.2

2. Find the range of each of the following data sets.
   (a) $C = \{9, 13, 15, 24, 32, 41\}$
   (b) $D = \{36, 22, 19, 50, 33, 6, 11\}$

Solution

(a) Range of set $C = 41 - 9$
$$= 32$$

(b) Range of set $D = 50 - 6$
$$= 44$$

3. The following table shows the distribution of the masses of 50 textbooks at a bookstore.

Mass (x g)	$300 < x \leqslant 500$	$500 < x \leqslant 700$	$700 < x \leqslant 900$	$900 < x \leqslant 1100$
Frequency	8	17	22	3

Find the range of the data.

Solution

The largest endpoint = 1100 g
The smallest endpoint = 300 g
∴ range of the data = 1100 − 300
$$= 800 \text{ g}$$

4. Consider the data set $F = \{11, 15, 16, 23, 28, 37, 43\}$. Find
   (a) the median,
   (b) the lower quartile and the upper quartile,
   (c) the interquartile range of the data.

Solution

(a)   11   15   16   23   28   37   43

$$\qquad\qquad Q_1 \qquad\qquad Q_2 \qquad\qquad Q_3$$

Median, $Q_2 = 23$

(b) Lower quartile, $Q_1 = 15$
Upper quartile, $Q_3 = 37$

(c) Interquartile range $= 37 - 15$
$$= 22$$

5. Consider the data set $H = \{62, 37, 41, 54, 23, 49, 36, 60, 44, 52\}$. Find the interquartile range of the data.

Solution

The data set in ascending order is

$H = \{23, 36, 37, 41, 44, 49, 52, 54, 60, 62\}$.

$$\qquad\qquad Q_1 \qquad\qquad Q_2 \qquad\qquad Q_3$$

Lower quartile = 37
Upper quartile = 54
Interquartile range = 54 − 37 = 17

6. The following frequency table shows the amounts of the weekly pocket money of 100 students.

Amount (x)	$0 < x \le 10$	$10 < x \le 20$	$20 < x \le 30$	$30 < x \le 40$	$40 < x \le 50$	$50 < x \le 60$
Frequency	8	11	23	30	18	10

(a) Find the lower quartile, median and upper quartile of the distribution.

(b) Find the interquartile range of the distribution.

Solution

(a)

Amount (x)	Cumulative frequency
≤ 0	0
≤ 10	8
≤ 20	19
≤ 30	42
≤ 40	72
≤ 50	90
≤ 60	100

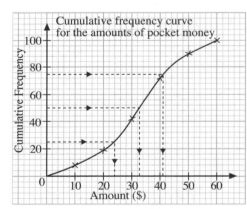

Cumulative frequency curve for the amounts of pocket money

$N = 100$

$\therefore \quad \dfrac{N}{4} = 25,$

$\dfrac{N}{2} = 50$ and

$\dfrac{3N}{4} = 75.$

Lower quartile, $Q_1 = \$24$
Median, $Q_2 = \$33$
Upper quartile, $Q_3 = \$41$

(b) Interquartile range $= \$41 - \$24$
$= \$17$

7. The following diagram shows the cumulative frequency curves for the masses of two batches of 500 chocolate bars produced by machines A and B respectively.

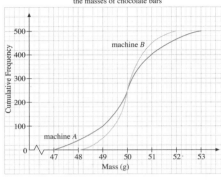

Cumulative frequency curves for the masses of chocolate bars

(a) For the chocolate bars produced by machine A, find
   (i) the range,
   (ii) the lower quartile, median and upper quartile,
   (iii) the interquartile range.

(b) For the chocolate bars produced by machine B, find
   (i) the range,
   (ii) the lower quartile, median and upper quartile,
   (iii) the interquartile range.

(c) The nominal mass of each chocolate bar is 50 g. Which machine is more reliable?

Solution

(a) **(i)** Range, $R_A = 53 - 47$
   $= 6$ g
   (ii) $N = 500$
   $\therefore \quad \dfrac{N}{4} = 125,\ \dfrac{N}{2} = 250,\ \dfrac{3N}{4} = 375.$
   Lower quartile, $Q_{1A} = 49.2$ g
   Median, $Q_{2A} = 50$ g
   Upper quartile, $Q_{3A} = 50.7$ g
   (iii) Interquartile range, $IQR_A = 50.7 - 49.2$
   $= 1.5$ g

(b) **(i)** Range, $R_B = 52 - 48$
   $= 4$ g
   (ii) Lower quartile, $Q_{1B} = 49.6$ g
   Median, $Q_{2B} = 50$ g
   Upper quartile, $Q_{3B} = 50.5$ g
   (iii) Interquartile range, $IQR_B = 50.5 - 49.6$
   $= 0.9$ g

(c) The median mass of chocolate bars from machine A and that from machine B are 50 g, same as the nominal mass.
Since $R_A > R_B$ and $IQR_A > IQR_B$, the masses of bars from machine A are more widely spread.
Hence, machine B is more reliable.

8. The noise level in a secondary school premise was tested and 400 readings at different times and locations were recorded. A report on the test provided the following information.

18 readings $\leqslant$ 50 dB
no readings $>$ 75 dB

The median noise level = 62 dB.
The lower quartile of the distribution = 54 dB.
The interquartile of the distribution = 12 dB.

(a) Find the upper quartile of the distribution.
(b) Draw a cumulative frequency curve of the distribution.
(c) Use your graph to find the 20th and 80th percentiles of the noise level.

Solution

(a) Interquartile range = $Q_3 - Q_1$
$$12 = Q_3 - 54$$
$\therefore$ $\qquad Q_3 = 66$ dB

(b) The following points are on the cumulative frequency curve:

(50, 18), (75, 400), (62, 200), (54, 100) and (66, 300).

A sketch of the cumulative frequency curve is shown below.

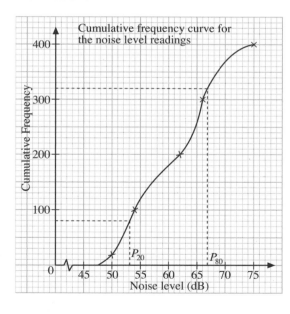

(c) $P_{20} = 20\%$ of $400 = \dfrac{20}{100} \times 400 = $ 80th term

$P_{80} = 80\%$ of $400 = \dfrac{80}{100} \times 400 = $ 320th term

$\therefore$ the 20% percentile, $P_{20} = 53$ dB;
the 80% percentile, $P_{80} = 67$ dB

Section 11.3

9. In an electrolysis experiment, the masses (in g) of a metal produced under certain conditions are measured. The results are summarised by a box-and-whisker plot as shown.

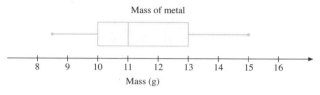

(a) State the median mass.
(b) Find the range of the masses of the metal.
(c) Find the interquartile range of the masses of the metal.

Solution

(a) The median mass = 11 g
(b) The range of the masses = 15 – 8.5
$\qquad\qquad\qquad\qquad\quad = 6.5$ g
(c) The interquartile range of the masses = 13 – 10
$\qquad\qquad\qquad\qquad\qquad\qquad\qquad = 3$ g

10. Siuli measured the volumes (in cm^3) of 12 eggs as follows:

53	60	62	68	70	71
74	75	80	83	85	87

(a) Find the lower quartile, median and upper quartile of the data.
(b) Represent the data by a box-and-whisker plot.

Solution

(a) Lower quartile = $\dfrac{62 + 68}{2}$
$\qquad\qquad\qquad = 65$ cm^3

Median = $\dfrac{71 + 74}{2}$
$\qquad\quad = 72.5$ cm^3

Upper quartile = $\dfrac{80 + 83}{2}$
$\qquad\qquad\qquad = 81.5$ cm^3

(b) The diagram below is the required box-and-whisker plot.

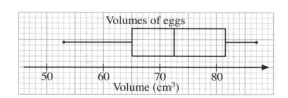

11. The following frequency table shows the distribution of the times taken by 50 people to complete an application form.

Time (t min)	$20 < t \leqslant 25$	$25 < t \leqslant 30$	$30 < t \leqslant 35$	$35 < t \leqslant 40$	$40 < t \leqslant 45$
Frequency	5	9	18	11	7

(a) Draw a cumulative frequency curve for the data.
(b) Find the lower quartile, median and upper quartile of the data.
(c) Draw a box-and-whisker plot for the data.

Solution

(a)

Time (t min)	Cumulative frequency
$t \leqslant 20$	0
$t \leqslant 25$	5
$t \leqslant 30$	14
$t \leqslant 35$	32
$t \leqslant 40$	43
$t \leqslant 45$	50

The diagram below shows the cumulative frequency curve for the data.

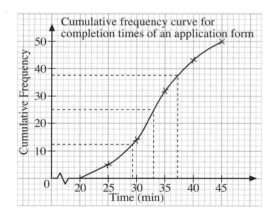

(b) $N = 50$

$\therefore \dfrac{N}{4} = 12.5$, $\dfrac{N}{2} = 25$ and $\dfrac{3N}{4} = 37.5$.

Lower quartile = 29.3 min
     Median = 33 min
Upper quartile = 37.3 min

(c) Minimum of the data = 20 min
Maximum of the data = 45 min
The diagram below shows the required box-and-whisker plot.

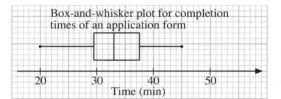

Exercise 11.1
Basic Practice

1. The cumulative frequency curve shows the speeds of 500 cars passing by a speed camera on an expressway. Use the graph to find
   (a) the number of cars with speeds less than or equal to 60 km/h,
   (b) the percentage of cars that were speeding if the speed limit was 70 km/h.

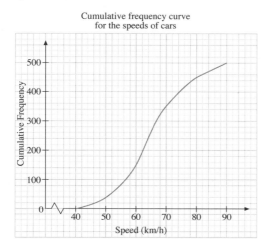

Cumulative frequency curve
for the speeds of cars

Solution
(a) Number of cars with speeds less than or equal to 60 km/h = 150

(b) Number of speeding cars = 500 − 350
$$= 150$$
The required percentage $= \dfrac{150}{500} \times 100\%$
$$= 30\%$$

2. 150 students were asked to solve a mathematical puzzle. The times taken by them were distributed as shown in the cumulative frequency curve.

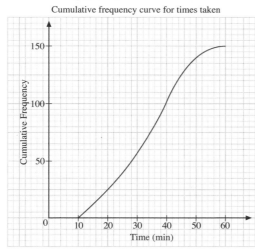

Cumulative frequency curve for times taken

From the graph, estimate
(a) the number of students who took more than 45 minutes to solve the puzzle,
(b) the percentage of students who took between 15 and 35 minutes.

Solution
(a) The required number of students = 150 − 125
$$= 25$$
(b) The required number of students = 78 − 12
$$= 66$$
The required percentage
$$= \frac{66}{150} \times 100\%$$
$$= 44\% \quad \text{(correct to 3 sig. fig.)}$$

Further Practice

3. The graph shows the cumulative frequency curve of the masses of 100 small parcels that arrived at a post office on a certain day.

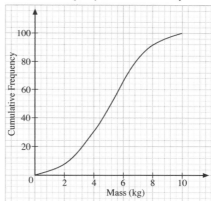

Cumulative frequency curve for masses of parcels

(a) Copy and complete the following cumulative frequency table for the data.

Mass (x kg)	$\leqslant 0$	$\leqslant 2$	$\leqslant 4$	$\leqslant 6$	$\leqslant 8$	$\leqslant 10$
Cumulative frequency	0	8	30	66	91	100

(b) Use your graph to estimate
   (i) the number of parcels with masses greater than 7 kg,
   (ii) the percentage of parcels with masses equal to 3 kg or less.

Solution
(b) (i) The required number of parcels = 100 − 82
$$= 18$$

(ii) The required percentage $= \dfrac{18}{100} \times 100\%$
$$= 18\%$$

4. The following diagram is the cumulative frequency curve for the Intelligence Quotient (IQ) of 300 students.

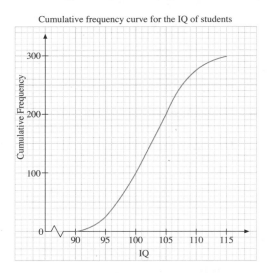

Cumulative frequency curve for the IQ of students

(a) Find the percentage of students with IQ of more than 100.

(b) Copy and complete the following frequency table for the distribution.

IQ (x)	90 < x ⩽ 95	95 < x ⩽ 100	100 < x ⩽ 105	105 < x ⩽ 110	110 < x ⩽ 115
Frequency					

(c) Draw a histogram for the distribution.

(d) Comment on the shape of the distribution.

Solution

(a) Number of students with IQ more than 100
= 300 − 100
= 200

∴ the required percentage = $\frac{200}{300} \times 100\%$

= $66\frac{2}{3}\%$

(b)

IQ (x)	Frequency
90 < x ⩽ 95	25
95 < x ⩽ 100	75
100 < x ⩽ 105	100
105 < x ⩽ 110	75
110 < x ⩽ 115	25

(c) The diagram below shows the histogram for the distribution.

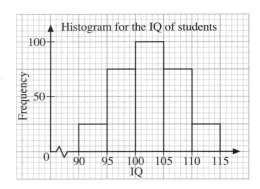

Histogram for the IQ of students

(d) The distribution is symmetrical with the peak at the middle.

Maths@Work

5. A botanist grew 400 plants in a controlled environment. The heights of the plants after two months are represented by the following cumulative frequency curve.

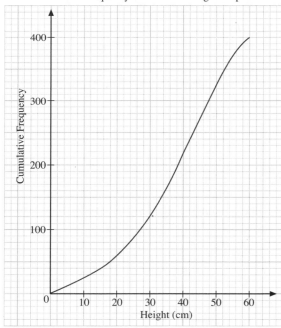

Cumulative frequency curve for the heights of plants

Use your graph to estimate

(a) the number of plants with heights greater than 45 cm,

(b) the percentage of plants with heights less than or equal to 18 cm.

Solution

(a) Number of plants with heights greater than
45 cm = 400 − 275
= 125

(b) Number of plants with heights less than or equal
to 18 cm = 50

The required percentage = $\frac{50}{400} \times 100\%$
= 12.5%

6. A quality control officer tested the lifetime (in hours) of
50 light bulbs of Brand A and 50 light bulbs of Brand B.
The results are shown in the given cumulative frequency
diagram.

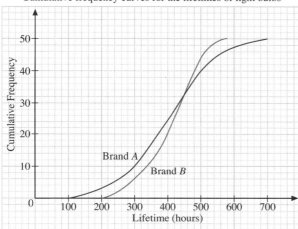

Cumulative frequency curves for the lifetimes of light bulbs

(a) State the brand of the light bulb which has the
longest lifetime among these 100 light bulbs.

(b) Light bulbs of lifetimes more than 400 hours are
said to be satisfactory. From the graph, estimate
the percentage of satisfactory light bulbs of
   (i) Brand A,
   (ii) Brand B.

Solution

(a) Brand A.

(b) **(i)** Number of satisfactory light bulbs
= 50 − 25
= 25

The required percentage = $\frac{25}{50} \times 100\%$
= 50%

(ii) Number of satisfactory light bulbs
= 50 − 21
= 29

The required percentage = $\frac{29}{50} \times 100\%$
= 58%

Brainworks

7. Construct a frequency table such that the shape of its
corresponding cumulative frequency curve is similar to
the one shown in the diagram.

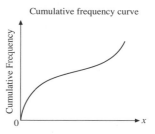

Cumulative frequency curve

Solution

Consider the following frequency table.

x	**Frequency**
$0 < x \leqslant 10$	20
$10 < x \leqslant 20$	10
$20 < x \leqslant 30$	5
$30 < x \leqslant 40$	5
$40 < x \leqslant 50$	10
$50 < x \leqslant 60$	20

Its corresponding cumulative frequency curve is as shown
below.

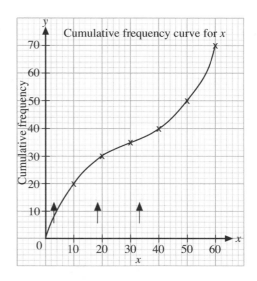

Cumulative frequency curve for x

Exercise 11.2
Basic Practice

1. For each set of data, find the range, lower quartile, median, upper quartile and interquartile range.
   (a) {6, 9, 13, 18, 21, 24, 33}
   (b) {12, 17, 19, 23, 27, 30, 35, 39}
   (c) {53, 62, 34, 71, 46, 39, 58, 66, 50}
   (d) {137, 258, 190, 231, 174, 206, 92, 168, 210, 153}

Solution

(a) {6, 9, 13, 18, 21, 24, 33}

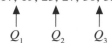

$Q_1 \quad Q_2 \quad Q_3$

$$\text{Range} = 33 - 6$$
$$= 27$$

Lower quartile = 9

Median = 18

Upper quartile = 24

Interquartile range = 24 − 9
$$= 15$$

(b) {12, 17, 19, 23, 27, 30, 35, 39}

$Q_1 \quad Q_2 \quad Q_3$

$$\text{Range} = 39 - 12$$
$$= 27$$

$$\text{Lower quartile} = \frac{17 + 19}{2}$$
$$= 18$$

$$\text{Median} = \frac{23 + 27}{2}$$
$$= 25$$

$$\text{Upper quartile} = \frac{30 + 35}{2}$$
$$= 32.5$$

Interquartile range = 32.5 − 18
$$= 14.5$$

(c) Arrange the data in ascending order.
{34, 39, 46, 50, 53, 58, 62, 66, 71}

$Q_1 \quad Q_2 \quad Q_3$

$$\text{Range} = 71 - 34$$
$$= 37$$

Lower quartile = 42.5

Median = 53

$$\text{Upper quartile} = \frac{62 + 66}{2}$$
$$= 64$$

Interquartile range = 64 − 42.5
$$= 21.5$$

(d) Arrange the data in ascending order.
{92, 137, 153, 168, 174, 190, 206, 210, 231, 258}

$Q_1 \quad\quad Q_2 \quad\quad Q_3$

$$\text{Range} = 258 - 92$$
$$= 166$$

Lower quartile = 153

$$\text{Median} = \frac{174 + 190}{2}$$
$$= 182$$

Upper quartile = 210

Interquartile range = 210 − 153
$$= 57$$

2. The cumulative frequency curve shows the waiting times of 80 passengers at a bus stop.

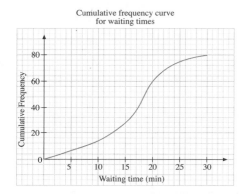

Cumulative frequency curve for waiting times

(a) Find the range of the waiting times.
(b) Find the lower quartile, median and upper quartile of the distribution.
(c) Find the interquartile range of the distribution.

Solution

(a) Range of the waiting times = 30 − 0
$$= 30 \text{ min}$$

(b) $N = 80$
$$\therefore \quad \frac{N}{4} = 20, \frac{N}{2} = 40, \frac{3N}{4} = 60.$$
Lower quartile = 12.5 min
Median = 17.5 min
Upper quartile = 20 min

(c) Interquartile range = 20 − 12.5
$$= 7.5 \text{ min}$$

3. The diagram shows the cumulative frequency curve of the marks of 60 students in a test.

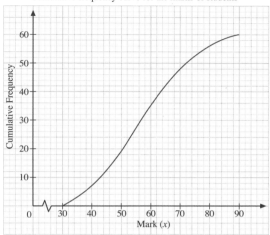

Cumulative frequency curve for the marks of students

(a) Find the range of the distribution of the marks.
(b) Estimate from the graph
    (i) the interquartile range,
    (ii) the 20th and 80th percentiles of the distribution.

Solution
(a) Range of the marks = 90 − 30
                     = 60 marks
(b) $N = 60$
    $\therefore \frac{N}{4} = 15$ and $\frac{3N}{4} = 45$.
    (i) Lower quartile = 47 marks
           Upper quartile = 67 marks
    $\therefore$ interquartile range = 67 − 47
                          = 20 marks
    (ii) $P_{20} = 20\% \times 60 = $ 12th term
          $P_{80} = 80\% \times 60 = $ 48th term
          $\therefore$ 20th percentile = 45 marks
               80th percentile = 70 marks

Further Practice

4. The diagram shows the cumulative frequency curve of the maintenance charges of 80 cars.

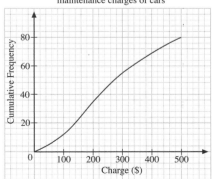

Cumulative frequency curve for maintenance charges of cars

Use your graph to find
(a) the lower quartile and upper quartile of the data,
(b) the interquartile range of the data,
(c) the 90th percentile of the data,
(d) the percentage of cars whose maintenance charges are between $100 and $300.

Solution
(a) $N = 80$
    $\therefore \frac{N}{4} = 20, \frac{N}{2} = 40, \frac{3N}{4} = 60$.
    Lower quartile = $140
    Upper quartile = $330
(b) Interquartile range = $330 − $140
                           = $190
(c) $P_{90} = 90\%$ of 80
         = 72nd term
    90th percentile = $420
(d) Number of required cars = 55 − 12 = 43
    The required percentage = $\frac{43}{80} \times 100\%$
                             = 53.75\%

5. A survey reported the number of hours that each of 400 students spent doing homework during one week. The results of the survey are shown in the cumulative frequency curve on the right.

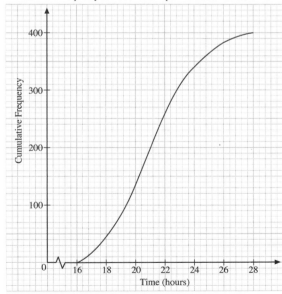

Cumulative frequency curve for times spent on homework in a week

(a) Find the range of the data.
(b) Use your graph to find the interquartile range of the data.
(c) If 30% of the students spent more than t hours doing homework, find the value of t.

Solution

(a) Range of the data = 28 − 16
           = 12 hours

(b) $N = 400$

$\therefore \frac{N}{4} = 100$ and $\frac{3N}{4} = 300$.

Lower quartile = 19.4 hours
Upper quartile = 22.8 hours
$\therefore$ interquartile range = 22.8 − 19.4
                     = 3.4 hours

(c) 30% of 400 = 120
120 students spent more than t hours means
400 − 120 = 280 students spent less than or equal
to t hours.
From the graph, $t = 22.4$.

Maths@Work

6. The following are the selling prices (in $) of a certain model of mobile phone in 15 stores.

300	305	298	278	320
317	290	328	300	280
285	300	280	299	310

(a) Find the mode and median prices of the model of mobile phone.
(b) Find the interquartile range of the data.
(c) Find the range of the data.

Solution

(a) Arrange the data in ascending order.
{278, 280, 280, 285, 290, 298, 299, 300, 300,

Q_1 Q_2

300, 305, 310, 317, 320, 328}

Q_3

Mode price = $300
Median price = 8th term
           = $300

(b)   Lower quartile = $285
            Upper quartile = $310
$\therefore$ interquartile range = $310 − $285
                        = $25

(c) Range of the data = $328 − $278
                 = $50

7. A restaurant manager investigated the turnaround times for the dining tables. The results are shown in the following diagram.

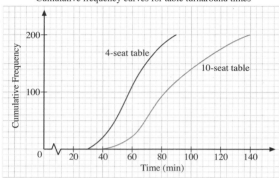

Cumulative frequency curves for table turnaround times

(a) Find the lower quartile, median, upper quartile and 60th percentile for the turnaround times of
     (i) 4-seat tables,   **(ii)** 10-seat tables.
(b) Comment on the results obtained in **(a)**.

Solution

(a) $N = 200$

$\therefore \frac{N}{4} = 50$, $\frac{N}{2} = 100$, $\frac{3N}{4} = 150$.

(i) For the 4-seat tables,
       lower quartile = 48 min
           median = 58 min
       upper quartile = 69 min
       60% × 200 = 120
       60th percentile = 62 min

(ii) For the 10-seat tables,
       lower quartile = 69 min
           median = 82 min
       upper quartile = 105 min
       60th percentile = 90 min.

(b) Interquartile range for 4-seat tables, IQR_A
     = 69 − 48
     = 21 min

Interquartile range for 10-seat tables, IQR_B
     = 105 − 70
     = 35 min

Since $IQR_A < IQR_B$, the spread of the turnaround times for the 4-seat tables is less than that for the 10-seat tables.

The median difference = 82 − 58
                  = 24 min

Since all the quartiles for the 4-seat tables are less than the corresponding quartiles for the 10-seat tables, the turnaround for the 4-seat tables is faster.

Brainworks

8. Greg recorded the distances of 500 of his golf shots, in metres. Some summary statistics of the distance distribution are shown below.

$$80 \text{ m} \leqslant \text{all distances} \leqslant 200 \text{ m}$$
The median distance = 145 m.
The lower quartile = 126 m.
The interquartile range = 32 m.
The 90th percentile = 173 m.

(a) Calculate
   (i) the range,
   (ii) the upper quartile of the distribution.
(b) Draw a cumulative frequency curve to represent the information.
(c) Use your graph to find the 40th percentile of the distribution.
(d) When Greg used a better quality club, each golf shot was 10 m further. Find the change in
   (i) the median,
   (ii) the interquartile range of the distribution.

Solution
(a) **(i)** Range = 200 − 80 = 120 m
   (ii) Interquartile range = $Q_3 - Q_1$
            $32 = Q_3 - 126$
            $Q_3 = 158$
         Upper quartile = 158 m
(b) The following points are on the cumulative frequency curve:

   (80, 0), (126, 125), (145, 250), (158, 375), (173, 450), (200, 500).

   The diagram below is the required cumulative frequency curve.

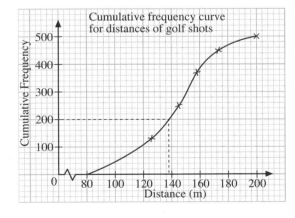

(c) $P_{40} = 40\% \times 500 = 200\text{th term}$
   $\therefore$ 40th percentile = 138 m
(d) **(i)** The median increased by 10 m.
   (ii) The interquartile range remained the same.

9. **(a)** Construct a frequency table with 200 values such that

   each value $\geqslant 10$,
   the median = 40,
   the lower quartile = 30,
   the range = 60,
   and   the interquartile range = 25.
(b) Draw a cumulative frequency curve for your data in **(a)**.

Solution
(a) A possible frequency table that fulfils the given conditions is as follows.

Data (x)	Frequency
$10 < x \leqslant 20$	20
$20 < x \leqslant 30$	30
$30 < x \leqslant 40$	50
$40 < x \leqslant 50$	40
$50 < x \leqslant 60$	20
$60 < x \leqslant 70$	40

(b) The diagram below is the cumulative frequency curve for the data.

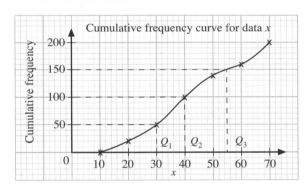

Exercise 11.3
Basic Practice

1. The following diagram shows the box-and-whisker plot of a data set.

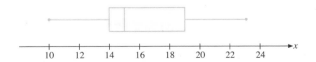

(a) State the lower quartile, median and upper quartile of the data set.
(b) Find the range of the data set.

Solution

(a) Lower quartile = 14
    Median = 15
    Upper quartile = 19

(b) Range = 23 – 10
    = 13

2. The following diagram shows the box-and-whisker plot for a data set.

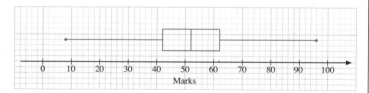

(a) Find the lower quartile and upper quartile of the data set.

(b) Compare the spread of data between the lowest 25% and the highest 25% of the data set.

Solution

(a) Lower quartile = 20
    Upper quartile = 33

(b) The spread of data is much wider in the lowest 25% of the data set than in the highest 25%.

3. The following diagram shows the box-and-whisker plot for the results (in marks) of a test.

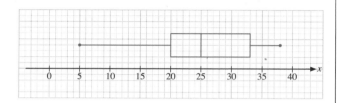

(a) Find the median and interquartile range from the box plot.

(b) Compare the spread of data within the interquartile range with the spread of the whole data set.

Solution

(a) Median = 52
    Interquartile range = 62 – 42
        = 20

(b) The spread of data within the interquartile range is narrow (within a range of 20) whereas the range of the whole data, which is 88, is wide.)

4. The diagram shows the box-and-whisker plot for the data set

$$\{5, 8, 13, 19, 21, 24, 28, 32, 37, 40, 45\}.$$

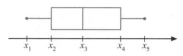

(a) Find the value of x_3.

(b) Find the value of $x_4 - x_2$.

(c) Find the value of $x_5 - x_1$. What does it represent?

Solution

The data set: 5, 8, 13, 19, 21, 24, 28, 32, 37, 40, 45

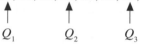

(a) $x_3 = 24$

(b) $x_4 - x_2 = 37 - 13$
        $= 24$

(c) $x_5 - x_1 = 45 - 5$
        $= 40$

The value of $x_5 - x_1$ represents the range of the data set.

Further Practice

5. The following diagram shows the cumulative frequency curve for the masses of 100 chickens in a farm.

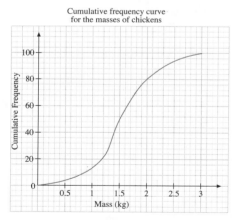

(a) Find the lower quartile, median and upper quartile of the distribution.

(b) The box-and-whisker plot for the distribution is shown on the right.

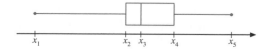

(i) Find the value of x_2 and x_5.

(ii) Find the percentage of chickens whose masses are between x_2 and x_5.

Solution

(a) $N = 100$

$\therefore \dfrac{N}{4} = 25, \dfrac{N}{2} = 50, \dfrac{3N}{4} = 75.$

Lower quartile = 1.25 kg

Median = 1.5 kg

Upper quartile = 1.85 kg

(b) **(i)** $x_2 = 1.25$ kg

$x_5 = 3$ kg

(ii) Number of chickens whose masses are between x_2 and x_5

$= 100 - 25 = 75$

The required percentage $= \dfrac{75}{100} \times 100\%$

$= 75\%$

---

6. The following diagram shows the box-and-whisker plots of two data sets, A and B.

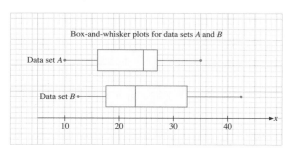

Box-and-whisker plots for data sets A and B

(a) Find the median, range and interquartile range of data set A.

(b) Find the median, range and interquartile range of data set B.

(c) Which data set has a higher median?

(d) Which data set shows a greater spread?

Solution

(a) For data set A,

median = 24.5

range = 35 − 10

= 25

interquartile range = 27 − 16

= 11

(b) For data set B,

median = 23

range = 42.5 − 12.5

= 30

interquartile range = 32.5 − 17.5

= 15

(c) Data set A has a higher median.

(d) Since range of $A <$ range of B and interquartile range of $A <$ interquartile range of B, data set B shows a greater spread.

Maths@Work

7. In a city, the amounts (in μg/m^3) of sulphur dioxide measured at 14 observation stations at a certain time were as follows.

41	24	21	37	25	19	13
8	56	43	14	16	71	36

(a) Find the range of the data.

(b) Find the lower quartile, median and upper quartile of the data.

(c) The diagram below shows the box-and-whisker plot of the data.

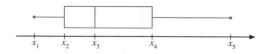

$x_1 \quad x_2 \quad x_3 \quad x_4 \quad x_5$

(i) State the values of x_3 and x_5.

(ii) The right whisker is much longer than the left one. What does this mean?

Solution

(a) Arrange the data in ascending order.

{8, 13, 14, 16, 19, 21, 24, 25, 36, 37,

$Q_1 \qquad\qquad Q_2$

41, 43, 56, 71}

Q_3

Range = 71 − 8

= 63 μg/m^3

(b) Lower quartile = 16 μg/m^3

Median $= \dfrac{24 + 25}{2}$

$= 24.5$ μg/m^3

Upper quartile = 41 μg/m^3

(c) **(i)** $x_3 = 24.5$ μg/m^3

$x_5 = 71$ μg/m^3

(ii) The distribution has a longer tail on the right.

8. The following diagram shows the box-and-whisker plots of the lifetimes of 60 cutting tools of brand *A* and brand *B*.

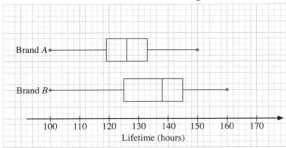

Box-and-whisker plots for the lifetimes
of brand *A* and brand *B* cutting tools

(a) Describe briefly these two distributions.

(b) If the cutting tools of brand *A* and brand *B* are sold at the same price, which brand would you prefer? Why?

Solution

(a) The distribution for brand *A* is quite symmetric with the peak at the middle.
The distribution for brand *B* has a longer tail to the left.
The median value for brand *B* is 12 hours higher than that for brand *A*.
Brand *A* has a wider spread.

(b) I would choose brand *B*. This is because its quartiles are higher than the corresponding quartiles of brand *A*. Therefore, if I buy a brand *B* cutting tool, it is more likely that its lifetime is longer than a brand *A* one.

Brainworks

9. A group of children were asked to guess the number of sweets in a bottle. Their guesses are recorded in the following stem-and-leaf plot.

Stem	Leaf
2	8 8 8 9 9 9 9
3	0 1 2 3 4 4 5 5 5 6 6 7
4	0 0 0 0 1 1 1 2 2 3 4 4

Key: 2 | 8 means 28

(a) Calculate the lower quartile, median and upper quartile of this distribution.

(b) Hence, draw a box-and-whisker plot.

(c) Suppose each sweet is a sphere of radius 1 cm and the bottle is a cylinder of base radius 2.5 cm and height 8 cm.

    (i) Find the volume of each sweet.

    (ii) Find the volume of the bottle.

    (iii) Based on the above information, would you guess the number of sweets in the bottle to be 40? Explain briefly.

(Express the answers for **(i)** and **(ii)** in terms of π.)

Solution

(a)
$$\text{Median} = \text{16th term}$$
$$= 35$$
$$\text{Lower quartile} = \text{8th term}$$
$$= 30$$
$$\text{Upper quartile} = \text{24th term}$$
$$= 41$$

(b) The diagram below shows the required box-and-whisker plot.

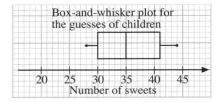

Box-and-whisker plot for
the guesses of children

(c) **(i)** Volume of each sweet $= \dfrac{4}{3}\pi \times 1^3$
$$= \dfrac{4}{3}\pi \text{ cm}^3$$

    (ii) Volume of the bottle $= \pi \times 2.5^2 \times 8$
$$= 50\pi \text{ cm}^3$$

    (iii) Let n be the number of sweets in the bottle.
Then $\dfrac{4}{3}\pi \times n \leqslant 50\pi$
$$n \leqslant 37.5$$
∴ the guess should not be 40.

10. Construct a cumulative frequency curve of values of x such that its box-and-whisker plot is as shown below.

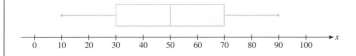

Solution

Consider the following cumulative frequency table.

x	Cumulative frequency
$x \leqslant 10$	0
$x \leqslant 20$	2
$x \leqslant 30$	10
$x \leqslant 40$	17
$x \leqslant 50$	20
$x \leqslant 60$	23
$x \leqslant 70$	30
$x \leqslant 80$	38
$x \leqslant 90$	40

Then its cumulative frequency curve is as follows in which minimum = 10, $Q_1 = 30$, $Q_2 = 50$, $Q_3 = 70$ and maximum = 90.

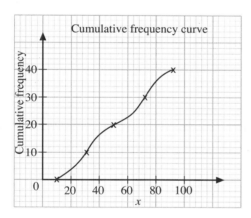

Revision Exercise 11

1. The readings of the air pollution index (API) of a city in 15 days were recorded as follows:

> 82 76 53 47 90 62 73 58
> 77 91 102 68 75 80 56

(a) Find the mean and the median of the data.
(b) Find the lower quartile and upper quartile of the data.

Solution

(a) Arrange the data in ascending order.
{47, 53, 56, 58, 62, 68, 73, 75, 76, 77, 80,

                            Q_1 Q_2

82, 90, 91, 102}

  Q_3

$$\text{Mean} = \frac{1}{15}(47 + 53 + 56 + \ldots + 102)$$
$$= \frac{1}{15} \times 1090$$
$$= 72\frac{2}{3}$$

Median = 75

(b) Lower quartile = 58
Upper quartile = 82

2. The following cumulative frequency curve shows the speeds of 60 cars passing by a junction.

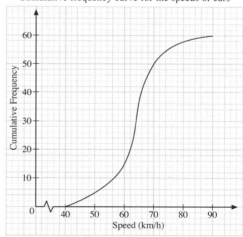

Cumulative frequency curve for the speeds of cars

(a) Find the median speed of the cars.
(b) If the speed limit at the junction is 70 km/h, find the percentage of cars that were speeding.
(c) What is the greatest speed of the slowest 20% of the cars?

Solution

(a) $N = 60$

$$\text{Median speed} = \frac{60}{2}\text{th term}$$
$$= 30\text{th term}$$
$$= 64 \text{ km/h}$$

(b) Percentage of cars that were speeding

$$= \frac{60 - 50}{60} \times 100\%$$

$$= 16.7\% \quad \text{(correct to 3 sig. fig.)}$$

(c) $20\% \times 60 = 12$

Hence, the greatest speed of the slowest 20% of the cars is 58 km/h.

---

3. The diagram below shows the cumulative frequency curve for the durations of 200 pop songs.

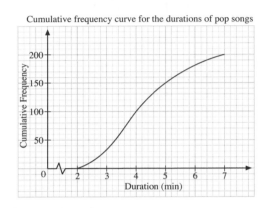

Cumulative frequency curve for the durations of pop songs

(a) Use your graph to find the median, lower quartile and upper quartile of the data.

(b) Find the range and interquartile range of the data.

(c) The box-and-whisker plot for the data is shown below.

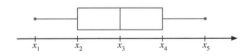

(i) State the values of x_2 and x_4.

(ii) What does $x_4 - x_2$ represent?

Solution

(a) $N = 200$

$$\therefore \frac{N}{4} = 50, \frac{N}{2} = 100, \frac{3N}{4} = 150.$$

Median = 4 min

Lower quartile = 3.3 min

Upper quartile = 5 min

(b) Range = $7 - 2 = 5$ min

Interquartile range = $5 - 3.3 = 1.7$ min

(c) **(i)** $x_2 = 3.3$ min

$x_4 = 5$ min

(ii) $x_4 - x_2$ represents the interquartile range.

---

4. A survey was conducted to find the volume of water a person drinks per day. The results of the survey are shown in the cumulative frequency curve below.

Cumulative frequency curve for the daily volumes of water drunk

(a) Find the median and the interquartile range of the data.

(b) Find the percentage of people who drink more than 3.5 litres of water per day.

(c) Find the 10th percentile of the data.

Solution

(a) $N = 80$

$$\therefore \frac{N}{4} = 20, \frac{N}{2} = 40, \frac{3N}{4} = 60.$$

Median = 1.8 litres

Lower quartile = 1.1 litres

Upper quartile = 2.7 litres

$\therefore$ interquartile range = $2.7 - 1.1 = 1.6$ litres

(b) Percentage of people drinking more than 3.5 litres

$$= \frac{80 - 71}{80} \times 100\%$$

$$= \frac{9}{80} \times 100\% = 11.25\%$$

(c) $10\% \times 80 = 8$

$\therefore$ 10th percentile = 0.5 litre

---

5. A survey of the annual incomes of 600 office staff in a city is represented by the box-and-whisker plot below.

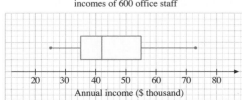

Box-and-whisker plot for the annual incomes of 600 office staff

(a) Find the lower quartile, median and upper quartile of the distribution.

(b) Find the range of the distribution.

Solution

(a) Lower quartile = $35 000
Median = $42 000
Upper quartile = $55 000

(b) Range = $73 000 – $25 000
= $48 000

6. The diagram below shows the box-and-whisker plots for the distributions of the masses of 100 women before and after joining a slim-and-fit programme.

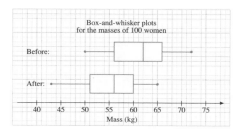

(a) Find the median, interquartile range and range of the distribution

    (i) before the programme,

    (ii) after the programme.

(b) What is the decrease in the median mass of the group of women after the programme?

(c) Which distribution has a greater spread?

(d) The masses of one of the women before and after the programme were 60 kg and 63 kg respectively. Can you say there is a mistake in the diagram?

Solution

(a) **(i)** For the distribution before the programme,
median = 62 kg
interquartile range = 66 – 56
= 10 kg
range = 72 – 50
= 22 kg

    (ii) For the distribution after the programme,
median = 56 kg
interquartile range = 60 – 51
= 9 kg
range = 65 – 43
= 22 kg

(b) Average mass loss = decrease in the median
= 62 – 56
= 6 kg

(c) Both distributions have the same range. But the interquartile range before the programme is greater than that after the programme by 1 kg. Therefore, the distribution before the programme has a greater spread.

(d) No, there may not be a mistake in the diagram. It is because the box plots only show some key statistics. The mass of an individual woman may increase after the slim-and-fit programme.

7. A quality control technician measured the diameters of 500 ball bearings produced by machine *A* and another 500 produced by machine *B*. The results are represented by the cumulative frequency curves below.

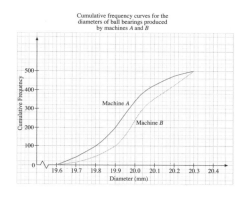

(a) Find the median and interquartile range for the diameters of the ball bearings produced by

    (i) machine *A*,   **(ii)** machine *B*.

(b) Which machine has less variability?

(c) Find the 70th percentile for the diameters of the ball bearings produced by machine *A*.

(d) Ball bearings with diameters less than 19.8 mm are considered defective. Find the percentage of defective ball bearings produced by

    (i) machine *A*,   **(ii)** machine *B*.

Solution

(a) **(i)** For the distribution of machine *A*,
median = 19.93 mm
lower quartile = 19.83 mm
upper quartile = 20.03 mm
∴ interquartile range = 20.03 – 19.83
= 0.2 mm

    (ii) For the distribution of machine *B*,
median = 20.01 mm
lower quartile = 19.925 mm
upper quartile = 20.13 mm
∴ interquartile range = 20.13 – 19.925
= 0.205 mm

(b) Since machine A has a smaller interquartile range,
∴ machine A has less variability.

(c) $P_{70} = 70\% \times 500 = 350$th item
∴ 70th percentile of the distribution of machine A
= 20.01 mm

(d) **(i)** Percentage of defective ball bearings from machine A

$= \dfrac{100}{500} \times 100\%$

$= 20\%$

(ii) Percentage of defective ball bearings from machine B

$= \dfrac{45}{500} \times 100\%$

$= 9\%$